Introduction to Culinary Arts Management

Safety, Recipes and Certification

T0392223

Written by **Dominic Hawkes** and **Daniel John Stine**

SDC
PUBLICATIONS

SDC Publications
P.O. Box 1334
Mission, KS 66222
913-262-2664
www.SDCpublications.com
Publisher: Stephen Schroff

Examination Copies	Books received as examination copies are for review purposes only and may not be made available for student use. Resale of examination copies is prohibited.
Electronic Files	Any electronic files associated with this book are licensed to the original user only. These files may not be transferred to any other party.
Trademarks	ServSafe is a trademark of the National Restaurant Association Educational Foundation. All other trademarks are trademarks of their respective holders.

The author and publisher of this book have used their best efforts in preparing this book. These efforts include the development, research and testing of the material presented. The author and publisher shall not be liable in any event for incidental or consequential damages with, or arising out of, the furnishing, performance, or use of the material.

Graphic design by Carter John Stine.

ISBN-10   1-63057-612-3

ISBN-13   978-1-63057-612-7

Printed and bound in the United States of America.

Intended Audience

Created for students in a culinary arts program, this book covers the wide range of food-related topics and provides weekly hands-on exercises and worksheets. At the conclusion of this course students will be prepared to take the ServSafe® Food Protection Manager certification exam.

Errata

Please check the publisher's website from time to time for any errors or typos found once printed. Simply browse to *www.SDCpublications.com*, and then navigate to the page for this book. Click the **View/Submit Errata** link in the upper right corner of the page. If you find an error, please submit it so we can correct it in the next edition. You may contact the publisher with comments or suggestions at *service@SDCpublications.com*.

Introduction

This book provides a collection of study materials to both learn about culinary arts and to prepare for the ServSafe® Food Protection Manager certification exam. With a range of options for most learning styles, this book will help improve your skill level and provide an additional boost of confidence, which is sure to increase the chances of a successful exam outcome. Study material for all learning styles provided, including:

Printed Coursebook

- Introduction to culinary arts *no previous experience required*
- Focused Study *on certification objective domains*
- Chapter summary *helpful study material*
- Glossary reference *orange text means that word is defined in the glossary*
- Food Code section reference *in margins supports further exploration of a topic*

Printed Student Workbook

- Personal copy *students can write in*
- Weekly exercises *supporting a full semester*
- Exercise-specific supporting video *featuring all necessary steps*
- Recipe worksheets *for each exercise*
- Forms and schedules *such as food cost worksheet & equipment lists*
- Flashcards *cut out with scissors*

Chapter Organization

- Objectives, key terms, etc.
- A day-in-the-life story
- Main contents - required reading
- End of chapter questions

Downloads

- Videos *with optional captioning*
- Practice Software *90 timed questions like the official exam*
- Downloads *accessible with code found in Student Workbook*

Practice Exam

The Student Workbook concludes with an overview of the included practice exam software download. This software mimics the real exam as much as possible, in terms of user interface, number and types of questions, as well as a time constraint. While this study guide cannot claim to cover every possible question that may arise in the exam, it does help to firm up your basic knowledge to positively deal with most questions... thus, leaving more time to reflect on the more difficult questions.

About the Authors

Dominic Hawkes is a Master Chef of Great Britain with over 29 years of experience in the food service industry. He began his culinary journey in London's finest hotels, including the Ritz, Radisson Edwardian & Prince Regent, and the Dubai International Aerospace Show. With a diploma in culinary arts, food hygiene, and certification in nutrition & health, and wines & spirits, Dominic later completed a bachelor's degree in business studies, majoring in hospitality studies.

After working for Bank of America's Corporate Food Services, Dominic became the Food & Beverage Director at Charlotte City Club, where he worked for 19 years before transitioning into teaching Culinary Arts. Since 2019, he has been teaching at the Lancaster County School District Career Center in South Carolina, where he is certified to teach and proctor four certifications by the National Restaurant Association, including ProStart Culinary & ServSafe.

Dominic's commitment to education is exemplified by his successful efforts in 2022 when he and the Lancaster County School District Career Center became the first secondary school in the Carolinas to receive American Culinary Federation accreditation, certifying students with the coveted Certified Fundamentals Cook (CFC) designation.

2020-21	2022-23	2022-23	2022-23
South Carolina ACTE New Teacher of the Year	South Carolina ACTE FYI New Teacher of the Year	South Carolina ACTE Culinary Award	EEA Best Practice & Knowledge Sharing Award

Dominic's dedication to his students was further highlighted during the 2020 pandemic lockdowns when he swiftly adapted his classes to an online platform. Since then, he has shared his valuable insights with audiences worldwide through his popular YouTube channel, Chef Hawkes. His tireless efforts in the culinary arts also earned him multiple accolades at the state and national levels, including his victory at the Carolina Classic Cook-Off and being featured on PBS Charlotte (WTVI).

Dominic is happily married to his awesome art teacher wife Courtney of 20+ years and has two amazing children, Jack & Tate. (Who followed different paths in Career & Technical Education (CTE) in high school too.)

Daniel John Stine is a certified ServSafe® food protection manager and a Wisconsin registered architect with over twenty years of experience. Daniel works at Lake | Flato, a top-ranked architecture firm based in San Antonio, Texas, USA. He has worked on many multi-million-dollar projects, plus a nearly $1 billion dollar hospital project in the Midwest. Throughout these years of professional practice, Stine has worked on many food service-related projects with commercial kitchens which require careful attention to the flow of food and food-related design codes and State/City/County health department regulations. He has also worked in multiple roles in the foodservice industry, including line and prep cook, dishwasher, server, and host.

He is a member of the American Institute of Architects (AIA), and the Illumination Engineering Society (IES), and serves on a national AIA Committee on the Environment (COTE) Leadership Group and was a co-author of the AIA Climate Action Business Playbook. Dan is also the chair of a national IES committee.

Daniel has 20 years of academic experience. Committed to furthering the design profession, Stine teaches interior design and graduate architecture students at North Dakota State University (NDSU) and has lectured for design programs at Penn State, Pratt Institute, Prairie View A&M, Northern Iowa State, University of Minnesota, & University of Texas at San Antonio (UTSA). As an adjunct instructor, Dan taught for twelve years at Lake Superior College in Minnesota. He has presented internationally on architecture and design technology.

With 20 years of experience developing content for the academic market, Stine has written 17 textbooks. These books are used in high schools, technical colleges, and universities across North America. His book *Residential Design Using Autodesk Revit* is the #1 Revit book in the academic market in North America. Five of Stine's books are focused on helping students become certified on various topics, including:

Table of Contents

Chapter 01

A World of Food

Every culture is defined by several things, such as its institutions, form of government, arts, customs, and even its food! While food is necessary to maintain life, it also can invigorate life and bring people together. When you think of weddings, births, promotions, and even the death of loved ones, people often gather around food — not just because it is necessary, but because it can be comforting or perhaps reminds us of "the old days". The multitude of things that happen to bring this food to our fingertips is the exciting adventure you are about to embark on in this exploration of the culinary arts!

Key Terms

Keep an eye out for these important topics:

- Front-of-house
- Back-of-house
- Full-time (FTE)
- Part-time (PTE)
- Culture
- Restaurant
- Roles
- Skills

Objectives

After working through this chapter, you should be able to explain the following to friends and family:

Rob,
Server

Rob has worked as a server at a local Tex-Mex restaurant chain for three years. He does not have a vehicle but lives close enough to walk to work. He works about 30 hours per week and enjoys the flexible hours and the opportunity to occasionally find a co-worker to cover a shift and take an extra day off. A typical work day is about 5 hours and involves waiting on 4-5 tables in a specific section.

As the primary facilitator of the customer's experience for the people he waits on, Rob greets them, takes their drink and food order, and facilitates payment. Although he does not prepare or cook the food, he must ensure everything looks correct and safe before serving the customer. Food Runners and Bus staff assist him.

Since the restaurant serves alcohol and some seafood items, he has received special training in both subjects. The state he works in requires any who sells alcohol to be a certain age and have a state issued bartender license. Regarding the seafood, his training included watching for signs of allergic reactions, such as hives or shortness of breath, and quickly calling 911 for emergency help.

Rob receives a paycheck every two weeks, like most jobs. In addition to his hourly rate, he also earns tips. Often, excellent & timely service results in better tips. On busy nights, like Friday and Saturday, he can make $100-250 in tips, some in cash, and some added to the credit card bill. The total money earned in tips must be entered into the computer when clocking out, as taxes are paid on all income.

Overall, Rob enjoys his career in foodservice and is interested in a managment role at the restaurant. He is a people person, and some of his co-workers have become good friends.

Roots of the Modern Restaurant

From a patron's perspective, a restaurant involves leaving home and paying to have a meal prepared for them at an establishment. The experience is nearly universally known; upon arrival, you are greeted by a **host**, and a table is requested. Once seated, a **server** welcomes you and caters to your every need, offering drinks, appetizers, entrees, and desserts listed on a **menu**. After the dining experience, the check is settled, and the customer is on their way.

It is not hard to imagine the value to the customer in this transaction. For example, the **time** saved preparing the meal, the possibility that they may not have the **skills/ingredients/equipment** to prepare certain dishes, and the effort required to **clean up** makes dining establishments very attractive. Don't forget people traveling, on vacation, or running errands and do not have time to prepare a meal. Add to this the elevated experience associated with **atmosphere**, **location**, and, let's not forget, the fantastic **tastes** offered by the perfect dish. It is easy to see how the foodservice industry thrives worldwide.

While this book focuses on the restaurant operation's perspective, which involves a fascinating orchestration of events that must happen—mainly in the background—with advanced **planning**, careful **management**, and precise **timing**, we will first reflect on the history of foodservice and when and how the modern restaurant came to be.

Although our focus in this chapter is on the Western history of food and restaurants, the notion of leaving one's home and 'eating out' has an incredible history that extends across the world, including ancient China and Egypt (northeast Africa). Therefore, let us first briefly reflect on our global roots.

Global Roots

While much of the illustrious culinary history of the world centers around western traditions, the simultaneous development of flavors, cooking techniques, and traditions occurring elsewhere is dramatic. The culinary world now benefits from everything from the best to the worst of human behavior. Examples include influences from seeds, like okra, brought in slave pockets from Africa to the Americas, and Spanish influences in Latin American cooking. Large portions of the western United States were part of Mexico, including Texas, New Mexico, Colorado, Utah, Nevada, Arizona, and California, until the Mexican-American war. Today, the results are seen and tasted in the strong Southwestern foods fusion, which is famous worldwide.

Sometimes similar foods were created on different continents, for instance, laminated doughs like the croissant in Europe and char siew sou in Southeast Asia. One did not influence the other, and both pastries are valid parts of their country's heritage and history. Tea is the most consumed prepared beverage on earth, with roots seen in the Indian subcontinent and Southeast Asia. These came to Europe with ceremonies adapted from their roots as their popularity spread. The historic spice trade continues to develop to this day, with seasonings available to us from around the world, enriching the dining experience. The result of humanity's movement around the globe has created a culinary community like never before. Agreements, deals, and wars have been resolved over food, as it has become a more social experience.

Western Roots

Families and tribes were primarily small and nomadic, so they gathered, hunted, and ate together. Over time, as populations grew and people became established in a particular location, they transitioned to an agrarian system, cultivating the land to produce more food closer to home. With more time, cities grew in size, some people became more affluent, and travel for work and pleasure became more common. Thus, feeding people presented itself as a business opportunity.

In ancient Rome, before being buried in volcanic ash by the eruption of Mt. Vesuvius in 79 A.D., Pompeii and Herculaneum had **Service Counters** (aka Thermopolium). Locals could purchase hot, ready-to-eat food on the side of the street. Consider how elements of this can be seen today in fast food, counter service at an amusement park, or (although mobile) a food truck.

Figure 1

In the early-1600s, the **American Inns** began offering a meal each day. Somebody could eat a meal at a large communal table at a specific time for a fixed price. This was not quite the restaurant we know today, as the customer did not have an opportunity to select from a list of entrées, and they could not show up whenever they were hungry. Instead, they ate what the cook chose, and if anyone arrived late, they did not eat. Even with these limitations and restrictions, the Inns served the community well at the time.

In the mid-1600s, the first coffeehouse was established in England. Like the local modern-day **coffeehouse**, these were a place people gathered to drink coffee and socialize. Back then, with the knowledge shared by patrons like Isaac Newton, they also became known as 'penny universities' as you could learn something for the cost of a cup of coffee.

In the mid-1700s, we find the birth of what we know today as the **restaurant**. In Paris, France, an eatery owner named Boulanger began offering "restorative" dishes such as hot bouillon or broth. The establishment was called a *restorante*, from which the contemporary word restaurant is derived.

Since France is the birthplace of the restaurant, it is no surprise we have so many transliterated French words associated with eating out here in North America. France is also home to the world-famous **Michelin Star** rating system, which recognizes restaurants worldwide for quality and creativity. The following are common French words associated with food:

- Café
- Dessert
- Chef
- à la carte
- Entrée

In the early 1900s, the National Restaurant Association was created in the U.S. and represents more than 500,000 restaurant businesses today. On behalf of its members and the foodservice industry, the organization advocates politically, provides research, and offers training programs. Its **ServSafe Food Protection Manager Certification** has certified over 10 million individuals over the past 30 years.

In the post-World War II era, a revolution began with the rapid rise of the family automobile. Quick service, also known as fast food, rapidly grew as the U.S. population gained wealth and more disposable income to enjoy dining out with higher frequency. By the 1970s, this spurred the need for nationally-recognized chain restaurants, as the public looked for food choices with known familiarity and traveled further afield. With the subsequent boom of transatlantic flight, the rapid expansion for many of these brands across Europe and beyond occurred, with numerous corporations being highly successful.

In the early 2020s, the global pandemic caused by the COVID-19 virus propelled **food delivery** to unprecedented levels. While home delivery of ready-to-eat food has been around for years, including pizza, subs, and groceries, the pandemic normalized this for the entire industry. Restaurants scrambled to convert lobbies into to-go packing assembly lines and created or expanded outdoor seating. Alongside this effort, food delivery apps such as Uber Eats and Door Dash became an essential thread between the customer and the foodservice industry, facilitating ordering, payment, and delivery of food and beverages. Many people returned to dining establishments post-pandemic to enjoy freshly plated foods, ambiance, and social interaction. However, the food delivery service is likely to remain popular and will only serve to bolster the overall reach and revenue of the professional foodservice industry.

A Career in Food

The foodservice industry provides a meaningful service to society. As such, many opportunities exist to build a short-term or lifelong career. A profitable business in or around food might be born for those with an entrepreneurial spirit. According to the U.S. Bureau of Labor and Statistics, over 4 million people are employed as "Food and Beverage Serving and Related Workers" alone.

In the U.S., the foodservice industry has nearly $1 billion in revenue annually. Americans spend more on eating out than on groceries, as shown in the USDA Economic Research Service graph below; however, the COVID-19 pandemic slightly reversed this trend.

People are motivated to become artists, musicians, doctors, or lawyers for various reasons. Similarly, the passion for food, interacting with people, and making them happy with a good meal and service can be a significant factor in a lifelong career in foodservice (good tips don't hurt either!).

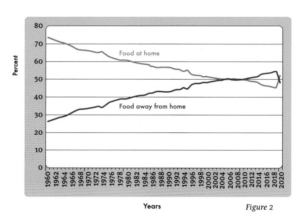

Years   Figure 2

The foodservice industry is known for offering flexible work hours. This does not mean someone can show up whenever they want to work, but it is often easy to find someone to pick up a shift to cover your hours. A colleague might even come in for their shift an hour or two early, so you can leave work early and not give up all your hours for a doctor's appointment. Restaurants often employ enough staff to accommodate this and others taking time off or calling in sick; staff should not feel compelled to work when they are ill.

Primary Employment

For business owners, their restaurant is not only their primary employment but also often thought of as "their life," given their passion for food and drive for success. Still, for many others, a career in food is their primary job. Individuals who have spent years in the industry become very skilled and often find promotion opportunities or move to establishments that offer advancement, higher pay, benefits, and increased tips.

A challenge with primary employment is the limited number of hours available to work each week. In the U.S., the IRS defines a **full-time** employee (FTE) as "an employee employed on average at least 30 hours of service per week, or 130 hours of service per month". Either way, the employer must pay certain payroll taxes such as social security (FICA) and federal/state unemployment taxes. However, based on several factors, such as the size and location of an organization, other benefits, e.g., health care, may be required for FTEs. Thus, hours are often limited to less than 30 hours per week to categorize most staff as **part-time** (PTE).

Another avenue for primary employment is within an institutional setting. For example, hospitals have large commercial kitchens to prepare food for patients and guests visiting the cafeteria. Some other examples are schools and large corporations. These positions often pay well, offer full-time hours, and include benefits such as health care, retirement, vacation time, and paid holidays.

Figure 3

Secondary Employment

Some people work in the foodservice industry for a second job. Or, following the previous discussion about limited hours in some organizations, the first job might also be in food. However, this secondary job might be in addition to an office job to make extra money. Maybe just around the holidays to proactively avoid credit card debt, be more physically active, or be social and interact with people such as co-workers and customers. You might even meet your future partner/spouse while working together in a restaurant, as one of the co-authors of this book did!

Temporary Employment

The possibility of temporary employment benefits both the employer and the employee. Employers often need a robust roster to ensure they remain fully staffed, especially during business hours. For many reasons, employees looking for temporary work can usually find it in foodservice with little to no previous experience, given the tradition of on-the-job training. Of course, the operation must always have experienced and certified staff on duty to educate, monitor, and mentor less-experienced workers.

Students often work in restaurants during their school years. Some students work during summer break, and others year-round. The range of children and young adults includes middle school, high school, and college students. Students who are 14 and 15 years old have certain restrictions on the number of hours they can work during the week, on school days, and even during summer break, according to the U.S. Department of Labor (for non-agriculture jobs). For students, a temporary food-related position might be a summer or their entire high school and college years.

The end-of-year holidays observed in the U.S., Thanksgiving, Christmas, and New Year, also represent a significant uptick in temporary employment in retail and foodservice. Again, in this case, the employer and employee mutually benefit from a temporary employment arrangement. The employee is interested in extra income at this time of year to help avoid the possibility of incurring credit card debt. The employer needs extra help during this busy time of year when people are out gathering with families, attending office parties, and shopping. While people enter the foodservice industry with the intention of the position being temporary, some might enjoy it enough never to leave.

Food—related Employment

Finally, many people work for companies that provide food-related services to restaurants, cafeterias, and catering services. The delivery/logistics companies offer products, such as raw ingredients and condiments. Other examples include sales representatives for distributers and products, kitchen equipment repair personnel, and marketing/graphic design professionals.

A Multitude of Roles

Many roles or positions within a restaurant perform specific tasks. Some are seen by the customer, while others work tirelessly in the background. In either case, the collective efforts of an operation's staff define it in terms of quality and reputation. Everyone has an important role to play. Below, we'll take a brief look at several positions common in the industry. Common restaurant positions include:

Host   Server   Bus staff   Cook   Prep cook

Dishwasher   Bartender   Food service manager   Supervisor

Host

The host is the first person a customer sees when they arrive. This person has multiple responsibilities, a big one often being to load-balance new tables across the available servers on duty. You may have been standing at the host stand, asking for a table, only to find a 5-10 minute wait. But looking past the host, you see several empty tables and wonder why there is a wait?

The idea of "load-balancing" benefits the server and the customer. A server often works on a fixed number of tables. Ideally, their tables would not all be seated simultaneously to provide optimal customer service. If each table's food were ready at once, the server would be hard-pressed to deliver it promptly while maintaining the ideal temperature. They would also be unable to check back with a table after receiving their food and see if everything is to their satisfaction.

The host also must be attentive to detail. If a customer has young children or an infant, they should seat them in a safe area and offer a booster or highchair. They may also need to ask questions about seating preferences, being proactive, so the customer does not have to ask. Common questions also include a seating preference for inside versus outside or in the bar area.

When there is a wait for tables, the host must closely track tables to see which appear nearly finished and which are being cleaned. This helps them give customers accurate wait times.

Server

Once a table is sat, meaning one or more customers are seated at a table, the server assigned to that table is now responsible for them and will cater to their needs. They typically have time guidelines for significant milestones in the customers' experience. For example, when the customer is first seated, the server should greet them and take their drink order within five minutes. When their food arrives, they should check back within 3 minutes to see if everything looks correct.

While some servers have a fantastic memory, most carry a notepad and take careful notes when the customer is ordering. Getting the customer's order right is essential, as some may have allergies, making "order taking" literally a matter of life and death.

Being a server can sometimes be intense, with the restaurant running at total capacity and people waiting in the lobby. During these times, we see them moving around rather quickly, focused on completing the next task. However, they should never rush to the point where they put themselves or the customer in danger. For example, they could slip on a wet floor and drop a plate of food on the customer, causing severe injury, lawsuits, or a workman's compensation claim for lost time at work and medical costs.

Foodservice Manager

The person who oversees all significant elements of a foodservice operation is the foodservice manager. They manage finances (payroll and paying bills), schedule staff shifts, order supplies, ensure policies and procedures are followed and handle staff complaints. They are often the most experienced and highest-paid.

Depending on the business size, some of these duties get delegated to assistant managers or senior cook/wait staff. Managing finances includes running sales reports, paying bills (rent, utilities, supplies, food products), and staff payroll. Sometimes the foodservice manager is also the owner of the business.

Bus Staff

Many people get their start bussing or cleaning tables in a restaurant. Bussing is an essential task in the overall operation of a restaurant. Once a customer leaves, the sooner a table is cleared and cleaned, the quicker the next group can be seated.

This job involves removing plates, utensils, and cups when the customer leaves and while the customer is dining.

Safety awareness must be keen as a dirty table may have knives, hot plates, drinks, and other hazards. Some of these hazards become concealed by stacked plates or cloth napkins. Items are carefully collected, so nothing is broken or spilled (especially when a spill might hit a nearby customer at another table).

Bussing tables requires some physical strength as all the items, which may have initially been brought out to the table at different times by the server, all need to be collected and carried to the dishwashing area. Of course, multiple trips should be made if necessary.

Cook (Chef)

Cooks prepare food ordered by the customer. They are either trained on the job or formally educated at a culinary school. A cook must multitask in a way that results in a food order all coming together simultaneously, so each item served is at the ideal temperature. This is often not just an order for one person but an entire table. All along, cooks must keep a careful eye on subsequent orders, which might have an item that takes longer to prepare/cook.

In addition to preparing food, a cook monitors several things to ensure food and staff safety. For example, the equipment must be working correctly to hold a food's temperature or cook a protein to the correct minimum temperature. Work areas must be kept clean and sanitized to prevent cross-contamination but also cleaned to avoid cross-contact. They must also take extra care when a customer identifies a food allergy.

The work of a cook can, at times, be busy. But they must always pace themselves, and be aware of their surroundings, to prevent injury to themselves and others. They work with sharp knives and are surrounded by hot objects and surfaces. The kitchen must be cleaned and sanitized at the end of each day. The waitstaff sometimes shares tips with the cooks.

Prep Cook

Prep cooks perform routine tasks to prepare for the day or keep an operation running smoothly during busy hours. Examples are cleaning and cutting raw ingredients such as fresh produce used to assemble dinner salads. Depending on the menu, large amounts of seasoned ground beef might be prepared and then held at the correct temperature on "the line" which contains an array of ingredients used by the cooks in a hierarchical order to facilitate assembling items such as burritos or tacos.

Figure 4

This position can involve starting early to ensure everything is ready for the cooks when the operation opens. Once prepared, items are stored properly to prevent the growth of bacteria or cross-contamination. This requires proper training and supervision over less-experienced staff. Like cooks and servers, prep cooks must keep their work area clean, sanitized, and safe.

Classic Kitchen Brigade

Larger and more sophisticated kitchens have many more specialized positions with specific titles. The graphic below highlights the classic kitchen brigade, which emphasizes the organizational structure. Ultimately, the executive chef is responsible for what happens in the kitchen and the food which leaves it.

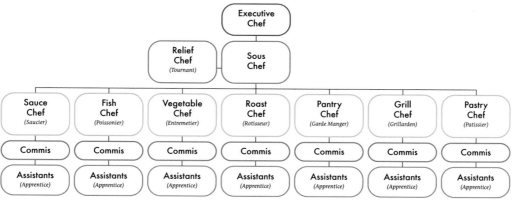

Figure 5

Dishwasher

Many people get their start as a dishwasher in a restaurant. While the tasks can vary, the goal is the same: clean all the pots, pans, and dishes, so they are ready to be safely used again. Some operations will only use a three-compartment sink, while others also have a commercial dishwashing machine. Each has particular ways they must be set up and used to achieve acceptable results.

The dishwashing machine is like a conveyor belt system, similar to some car washes. Dirty plates and cups are placed on racks, pushed into the machine, and emerge clean and hot on the other side. Some menu items are cooked directly on the plates, which may require the dirty plate to be scraped and scrubbed before running through the dishwasher. If there is still debris on the dishes or cups, they must be scrubbed by hand and run through the machine again.

Dishwashers often have other tasks like collecting the trash throughout the kitchen once an hour and taking it to the collection containers outside. Smaller operations might not have a dedicated dishwasher. This responsibility is shared by the cooks, wait staff, or host.

Bartender

When a restaurant serves alcohol, they often have a bar run by a bartender. The job involves mixing drinks based on a menu or request and then serving them directly to the customer or through wait staff. Many states require bartenders to be at least 18 years old, and some require a license/certification, which shows they have had basic training—on safety, age requirements, and related laws.

Like the kitchen, the bar area must be kept clean, sanitized, and safe. Spills must be cleaned immediately, not waiting to finish an order. Slippery floors present serious injury risks. And while the person who caused the spill *might* remain aware of it, a co-worker might approach suddenly.

Food is often served at the bar, which might be the full menu or select items such as appetizers. In this case, the bartender also fills the server role previously described.

The industry has many more roles, depending on location, style, and venue. All the positions discussed can be reduced to just a few people in smaller operations, such as a food truck.

Figure 6

Skills Required

Although these various roles, in almost any foodservice operation, have certain tasks and often require training and specific skills, there are fundamental activities all must support for safety and liability reasons. Everyone is involved in safety and should help quickly clean up a spilled drink to avoid accidents. Facilities serving alcohol must be aware of underage ordering or drinking and anyone who might be too intoxicated (these requirements vary by jurisdiction). Below, we'll take a brief look at common skills required in the industry. The following are a few common skills required:

Communication skills	Physical Stamina
Customer-service skills	Physical Strength

Communication Skills

Everyone in foodservice should have good communication skills, even those not working directly with customers. Cooks often actively talk to each other to orchestrate multiple orders and let each other know when they are passing by, calling out "behind you" so no one gets hurt or spills food. But those who work with customers must be able to take orders and know when to ask questions if you think there is any confusion. **Active listening** is an essential part of good communication skills.

Customer–service Skills

Good communication skills are a sub-set of good customer skills. Additionally, anyone in the service industry needs to be able to work with a wide range of customers. Some customers may be overly talkative, introverted, quiet, or angry. Good customer skills help ride the tide, or ups and downs, experienced daily. For example, when a customer is visibly or audibly upset, it is best to keep calm and not escalate the situation by showing signs of frustration. When an issue cannot be resolved quickly, the manager should be included to help deal with a problem.

Some organizations will offer, or require, customer service skills training. The topics covered may seem like common sense, but working through situations in an organized fashion can help enhance automatic responses to various situations. This training and experience will benefit people in all aspects of life and possible future careers.

Physical Strength

Most roles in the foodservice industry usually require a certain amount of physical strength and mobility. Trays of food and containers of dirty dishes can weigh 10-30 pounds (4.5–13.6 kg) and must be carried across the restaurant. It is essential to be aware of personal limitations and make an extra trip to avoid hurting oneself or putting others nearby in danger.

Physical Stamina

Different from physical strength is the need to have good physical stamina. A busy or popular food establishment may run at full capacity for an entire shift, which means the employees are working non-stop, also at full capacity. Stamina is the ability to perform continuously at a certain level and not become too tired to keep up with the job's demands.

Although physical strength and stamina are required to perform most duties in a foodservice establishment, people with disabilities must be provided reasonable accommodations per the protections afforded by the Americans with Disabilities Act (ADA). Also, during the interview and hiring process, the topic of a disability cannot be discussed pre-or post-job offer. Once hired, a disability may only be addressed as relevant to the required job duties and to facilitate any workplace environment changes.

> **"Does the ADA require that employers provide reasonable accommodations to qualified job candidates and employees with disabilities?"**

Yes. A reasonable accommodation is a change in the work environment or in the way a job or parts of a job are customarily done that enables a person with a disability to enjoy equal employment opportunities.

The Anatomy of a Restaurant

The following section will cover the terms and definitions of a restaurant's physical and functional areas. This can vary a lot depending on the type of operation and location. In any case, the following elements are often typical, even fundamental to the overall flow of a foodservice operation. This information will help set the stage for the remainder of the book.

Entrance (Host Stand)

When customers arrive at a restaurant, they enter the lobby and are welcomed by a host. The lobby also doubles as a waiting area. Entrance areas include:

Lobby/Waiting area   Hosting stand

Waiting Area

When a table is not immediately available, the lobby is also a waiting area with seating. Depending on the weather, guests may venture outside while they wait. They must remain close enough to the host stand to hear their name called when their table is ready. Sometimes the operation will have a speaker system or offer guests a handheld buzzer to notify them a table is ready.

Hosting Stand

The host works at the hosting stand. Here, he/she/they have a map of the dining area, with each table having a unique number. The tables are grouped, by server, to track which tables are occupied and when each server's last table was sat to spread out the workload. There is often a microphone to announce when tables are ready, and a phone to call for assistance or a manager.

Front-of-house (Dining Areas)

The part of the restaurant the customer sees and has access to is called front-of-house. Front-of-house areas include:

Outdoor Dining

Some restaurants offer outdoor seating, which may be adjacent to the dining room or the bar. Outdoor seating creates increased capacity for the operation without the high cost of a building and air conditioning typical of an indoor space. Of course, these spaces are weather dependent and come with their challenges. For example, it could start raining suddenly, or birds might be problematic.

Dining

Customers spend most of their time sitting at a table in the dining room. Dining might be one room or broken up into separate areas to manage noise, create different teams, or just fit the unique layout of the building. These spaces often have lower lighting levels for ambiance and have music playing lightly in the background.

Figure 7

Bar

The bar area often has a traditional bar with stools and an adjacent area with tables and chairs, like the dining room. This area is usually adjacent to the lobby as all, or part, of the bar is available for self-seating.

Figure 8

Restrooms

If a restaurant is a standalone operation in a building by itself, then customer-accessible restrooms are required. These restrooms must be handicapped accessible as well, according to the Americans with Disabilities Act (ADA), state and local laws, and building codes. However, the customer may have to leave the restaurant when it is located in a larger venue like a shopping center or resort.

Back-of-house

The part of the restaurant usually not seen by the customer is called the back-of-house. Back-of-house areas include:

Receiving

Receiving is a dedicated area for deliveries to be dropped off and inspected. It may be connected to a loading dock at a standalone facility or an elevator or hallway within a larger venue such as a shopping center or resort. This space is designed to stack product and properly inspect it, which requires space and adequate lighting levels (from natural or electric lighting).

———— *Design strategy* ————

Located close to an exterior entrance with good light levels. Receiving is positioned near storage to reduce travel distance. A good design also avoids passing through other back-of-house sections, which might interfere with production and create additional hazards.

Storage (dry/cold)

Back-of-house storage is often referred to as dry and cold storage, consisting of three separate spaces: dry, refrigerated, and frozen. Dry storage contains items at room temperature, like canned goods, onions, and ultra-high-temperature (UHT) pasteurized condiments. This room should be cool and not exposed to direct sunlight. Cold storages are held at or below 41°F (5°C) and keep items such as milk, produce, and eggs cold. Freezers are held at 0°F (-18°C) and store products like raw/cooked meats and ice cream.

———— *Design strategy* ————

Located near receiving and preparation for convenient stocking and access. Spaces must be appropriately sealed (and insulated) to conserve energy and keep pests and rodents out. A separate storage area must be available for chemicals and soiled/recalled food items.

Preparation

Before regular customer operating hours, prep cooks work to prepare pastries, desserts, sides, salads, and more. These items often take more time and might even be an ingredient in an entrée, but they also remain fresh longer and therefore can be prepared ahead of time once or twice a day. Since there may be some overlap with the production area and employ different equipment, they are separate but adjacent spaces.

———— *Design strategy* ————

Located between storage and production with a dedicated handwashing station. Requires specific equipment and tables (work areas) with quality lighting for working with sharp knives and other tools. Some equipment requires special electrical and plumbing connections and ventilation hoods above to exhaust steam, smoke, and excessive odors. The floors and free-standing equipment must be easy to clean under and around.

Service

When a table's order is ready, the server has an area adjacent to the production area to collect the dishes on a tray or cart. This area is often separated from the production area by a long stainless-steel unit with work surfaces and cold/hot holding, and more on the cook's side. Above this, partially under a heat lamp to keep food warm for a few minutes, is where the cooks place completed dishes. On the server-side, there is a place for their serving tray as they load it with plates. Adjacent to this would be utensils (steak knives) and condiments (ketchup) needed for specific orders or requests.

——— *Design strategy* ———

Located between production and the dining room, with the entrance close to dishwashing, and a handwashing station. A dedicated entrance and exit results in safe and optimized circulation. Requires ample space to collect large orders. May have coolers to hold pre-prepared salads and canned/bottled drinks. A soda dispenser and ice machine are typical as well.

Production (Kitchen)

Although everything just covered in this section is technically part of the kitchen, the production area is often simply referred to as the kitchen. This is a work (or production) space optimized for the type of menu offered. Ovens, fryers, microwaves, and hot and cold holding compartments adjacent to work surfaces are included. Cooks use all of this, plus ingredients and tools stored below counter cabinets, to prepare meals in bulk (e.g. at a hospital or cafeteria) or made-to-order (at a restaurant or food truck).

——— *Design strategy* ———

Located between preparation and service with a dedicated handwashing station. Requires specific equipment and tables (work areas) with quality lighting for working with sharp knives and other tools. Some equipment requires special electrical and plumbing connections as well as ventilation hoods above to exhaust steam, smoke, and excessive odors. The floors and free-standing equipment must be easy to clean under and around.

Figure 9

Dishwashing and cleaning

Dishwashing is a separate area used throughout the day and sometimes by dedicated staff. Items are easier to clean when attended to right away, which minimizes food remnants that could attract pests and rodents, and an operation rarely has enough pots, pans, plates, and glasses to not "clean as you go"! This area typically has a handwashing station, a three-compartment sink, and a commercial dishwashing machine. Additionally, there are wire-framed shelves to stack freshly cleaned and dried pots, pans, plates, and glasses.

─────── *Design strategy* ───────

Located adjacent to preparation, production, and service with a dedicated handwashing station. Between dishwashing and service, there is often a place for servers/bus staff to empty plates and sort/stack them. On the other side of this drop-off area is an adjacent sink to scrape and rinse plates and glasses before sending them through the conveyor belt-type dishwashing machine.

Office

The manager's office is in the back-of-house, near service (it does not require a dedicated handwashing station!). This space looks like a typical office, with a desk and computer. The manager, and assistant managers, will use this space to run reports and place orders. It may also be used to meet with staff and interview potential new employees.

─────── *Design strategy* ───────

Located adjacent to service. It should be large enough for a desk and two side chairs. This space may also contain a safe to keep important documents and start-of-day cash. A good design includes a window adjacent to the door to see the service and production area, keeping an eye open for problems and helping when things get backed up. Like school environments, the window also allows staff to see the manager and anyone else who might be in the office, which can help to avoid inappropriate behavior.

Breakroom

Adjacent to the service area, the breakroom is an area to sit and relax. In most jurisdictions, employees who are paid hourly must be given a certain number of 15-minute breaks depending on the length of their shift. Longer shifts also include a 30-minute lunch break. And while a person is not obligated to remain at the operation during this break, they typically do not have enough time to go anywhere. So the breakroom is where they sit, look at their phone, or read a magazine or book. Staff breaks are intentionally staggered to keep service going; thus, the breakroom only needs to accommodate a smaller percentage of on-duty staff. The breakroom may have lockers staff can use to store personal belongings while they work, like a jacket or purse. Employees whose shift includes a lunch break may receive a free or discounted meal.

Staff Restrooms

A staff-only restroom can often be found adjacent to the breakroom. To prevent food contamination, each sink has a sign stating "employees must wash their hands before returning to work".

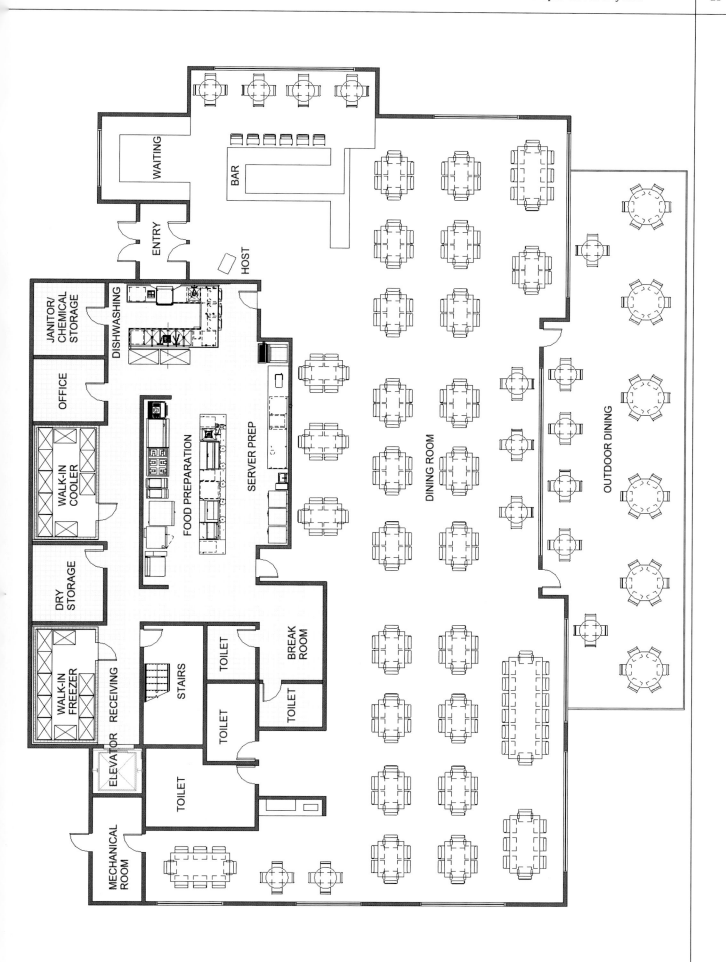

Summary

Even if you still don't see a career in the foodservice industry for yourself after working through this chapter, or the entire book, you will have a better appreciation for all involved in the process. From the facilities and equipment to the acquisition and storage, as well as cooking and serving, there are a lot of moving parts. All of these must be managed carefully to protect the customer, the reputation of the operation, and let's not forget the time-honored tradition that has helped shape community and family traditions and even define many cultures.

- The coffee shop, café, and restaurant have deep roots in Western civilization dating back to the 1600s. Gathering around food is a time-honored tradition all around the world.

- A career in the foodservice industry can be rewarding and lead to unexpected opportunities and places in the world.

- Food employees must have good customer skills, including good communication skills.

- The fast-moving environment often requires physical strength and stamina.

- Workers with disabilities have certain rights afforded by the Americans with Disabilities Act (ADA).

- Supporting safety and efficiency, the foodservice industry has specific terms for staff roles, spaces within the operation, and equipment.

The Student's Workbook

As assigned by your instructor, use the separate Student's Workbook to work independently or in groups. Activities for this week's chapter include:

- Who is your idol assignment & presentation.
- Kitchen tour of large foodservice equipment.
- Kitchen tour of smallwares & kitchen knives.
- Kitchen safety rules.
- Correct attire for the kitchen.

Review Questions

Use these questions to check your knowledge of the material in this chapter. *Your instructor has the answers.*

1 When first entering a restaurant, you are greeted by the _____.

a. server
b. host
c. manager
d. bartender

2 Food made before a restaurant opens is done by the _____.

a. cook
b. manager
c. prep cook
d. bus staff

3 Which is not a French word?

a. Café
b. Dessert
c. Kitchen
d. Entreé

4 The back-of-house is a term commonly used for the _____.

a. basement
b. bar
c. kitchen
d. dining room

5 The ServSafe Food Protection Manager Certification was created by the _____.

a. National Restaurant Association
b. Food and Drug Administration (FDA)
c. U.S. Department of Agriculture (USDA)
d. American Foodservice Alliance (AFA)

6 The IRS considers an employee full-time when they work more than _____ hours per week.

a. 20
b. 40
c. 35
d. 30

7 The first position in a restaurant is often as a _____.

a. server
b. manager
c. bus staff or dishwasher
d. cook

8 The person with the most responsibilities is the _____.

a. server
b. bartender
c. prep cook
d. manager

Chapter 02
Handling Food Safely

Much of what this section covers will sound like common sense and might be what many people already do at home when cooking. However, given the fast-paced environment and the potential dangers to consumers, especially the highly susceptible population (HSP) or those with allergies, safe food handling best practices in the foodservice industry cannot be left to chance.

The United States (U.S.) Food and Drug Administration (FDA) created and maintains the Food Code, which they recommend state and local jurisdictions adopt to protect food employees and the public from physical and foodborne illness dangers. Every food employee must thoroughly understand safe food handling through training, practice, enforcement, and consistent corrective action. By doing so, everyone will work as a team, and muscle memory will kick in when things get busy or distracting.

Key Terms

Keep an eye out for these essential topics:

- Protective coverings
- Restrict and Exclude
- Highly Susceptible Population (HSP)

- Ready-to-eat Foods (RTE)
- Personal Hygiene
- Carrier

- Corrective Action
- Handwashing
- Jaundice

Objectives

After working through this chapter, you should be able to explain the following to friends and family:

Lin,
Managing Owner

Lin owns a small dumpling shop in the heart of New York City. He has 5 dedicated employees who work hard to meet the demands of the busy business that is open seven days a week. Although Lin expects hard work, they are all paid well and enjoy the number of hours they work. But one day, Lin discovered one of his employees had the wrong idea about how dedicated he needed to be.

As Lin walked past the employee restroom to grab more produce from storage, he heard a strange sound. On his way back to the kitchen, John came out of the restroom. Lin asked if he was all right as he thought he heard what sounded like vomiting. John said he did in fact vomit, but felt better and could for sure finish his shift. He only had one hour left to work and it was during a busy lunch rush.

Lin knew that the FDA Food Code requires any employee who experienced vomiting, diarrhea, or jaundice to be excluded from work immediately. Lin said he appreciated John's desire to work hard but his health and the safety of the customer are more important. Lin sent John home and instructed him to not return until 24 hours after his symptoms had passed. With one less person, the team pushed through the rush and two days later John was back and thankful to have had the time to recover properly.

References in this Coursebook:

Glossary reference: Orange text means the definition of the word can be found in the Glossary located in the Student Workbook.

Food Code section reference: To verify or further study topics covered in this Coursebook, the FDA Food Code section numbers are provided in the margins. The current version of the offical code may be download here: https://www.fda.gov/food/retail-food-protection/fda-food-code

Why It Matters

The global COVID-19 pandemic has taught us that a virus (or microorganism) can and will spread, despite our best efforts. When handling food, over 40 kinds of bacteria, parasites, viruses, and molds (collectively called pathogens) can spread and contaminate food, causing foodborne illness. The stakes are high as about 48 million people a year experience foodborne illness, 128,000 are hospitalized, and roughly 3,000 die, according to the Centers for Disease Control (CDC). People sometimes describe a foodborne illness experience as having food poisoning or the stomach flu. Here are a few examples of how a food handler can contaminate food:

- Poor personal hygiene
- Improper handwashing
- Working while sick
- Bare hand contact with ready-to-eat (RTE) foods

KEY TERM Foodborne Illness is an illness caused by a harmful contaminant in consumed food.

Food safety is in the hands of the food employee. They must handle food safely to prevent the spread of contaminants through food. The ability to do so begins with training.

Personal Hygiene

People who work with or around food must start each day personally clean, including their **skin**, **hair**, and **outer clothing**, to minimize the spread of pathogens. Personal cleanliness is necessary to prevent contaminating food, equipment, and utensils. Managers will exclude or restrict staff, preventing or limiting them from working if they are not clean when they arrive. Employees should have multiple sets of work clothes or uniforms, or they must wash them between shifts.

2-304.11

People who prepare and handle food need to keep their fingernails trimmed, filed, and maintained, so the edges and surfaces are cleanable and not rough. Fingernail polish or artificial fingernails are prohibited unless wearing single-use gloves.

2-302.11

Jewelry is prohibited while preparing food, except for a simple wedding band. This includes medical information jewelry on the arms, such as a bracelet. It is difficult to clean around jewelry properly, and it is dangerous to lose it in the food and possibly harm a consumer.

2-303.11

Smoking, vaping, chewing gum, or tobacco products is prohibited except in designated areas away from food preparation areas and typically outside.

2-401.11

Handwashing

To effectively reduce the spread of pathogens from an employee's hands to food, handwashing must be performed appropriately. The steps to effectively wash hands are shown in the adjacent graphic. Care must be taken not to re-contaminate hands; thus, use a paper towel to turn off the faucet and open the restroom door. It is vital to scrub around the fingernails, as they are often the most contaminated part of the hands since they are the most difficult to clean. Each handwashing step is essential and should be performed consistently to minimize the potential of contaminating food. To wash hands or prosthetic devices correctly, use the steps on the following page. The whole process should take at least 20 seconds.

5-202.12

Starting with the 2022 Food Code, the water temperature at a handwashing sink must be 85°F (29.4°C) or higher. The goal is comfort, as food handlers are less likely to wash their hands if the water is too hot or cold. For handwashing, soap is what inactivates pathogens, not the water temperature.

In addition to knowing how to properly wash hands, it is equally important to know when and where to do it.

Where to Wash Hands

2-301.15

Hands may only be washed in a handwashing sink or approved automatic handwashing facility. Everything else is excluded, like a three-compartment sink, mop sinks, or sinks used for food preparation. Proper separation of hand washing and other sink-related tasks helps prevent cross-contamination which can lead to foodborne illness.

Figure 1

KEY TERM Cross-Contamination occurs when a pathogen, chemical, or physical substance has been transferred to a food or beverage. The result can be potentially harmful, causing foodborne illness if consumed.

2-301.12

1   Rinse under clean, warm running water.

2   Apply soap.

3   Rub all surfaces of the hands and fingernails together vigorously for at least 10 to 15 seconds.

4   Rinse thoroughly with clean, warm running water.

5   Thoroughly dry the hands and exposed portions of arms.

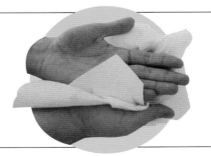

Figure 2

When to Wash Hands

2-301.14

Food handlers should wash their hands immediately after engaging in activities that contaminate the hands and:

- When entering a food preparation area
- Before putting on clean, single-use gloves for working with food and between glove changes
- Before engaging in food preparation
- Before handling serving utensils and clean equipment
- When changing tasks and switching between working with read-to-eat foods or handling raw foods
- After touching soiled equipment, dishes, utensils, or mobile device (cellphone)
- After touching bare human body parts, like arms, ears, or nose - except clean hands and arms
- After using the restroom or toilet
- After sneezing, coughing, blowing the nose, using tobacco products, drinking, or eating
- After caring for or handling aquatic animals such as molluscan shellfish or crustacea in display tanks or service animals
- After any activities that contaminate the hands

Figure 3

Hand Antiseptics

2-301.16

Hand antiseptics, used as a topical application, may be found within a restaurant but are technically optional and cannot be used in place of proper handwashing, so it is essential to know what this is and when it may be used. Hand antiseptic, also known as hand sanitizer—liquid or gel—is not a triple-antibiotic, such as Neosporin, used to treat a wound. Instead, it is a disinfectant that removes pathogens from the surface of the hands. However, its effectiveness is varied depending on the amount of contamination and physical debris on the hands and fingernails. If used, **only use it after washing hands, let it fully dry, and never in place of proper handwashing**.

Figure 4

Manager's Responsibility

Ultimately, the food establishment manager is responsible for the personal hygiene of their employees. They are required to train and monitor food employees for proper personal hygiene. **Corrective actions** are required when workers are not following procedure by immediately being corrected and retrained. Additionally, contaminated food must be discarded, and tainted equipment **must be** cleaned and sanitized.

2-103.11(D)

Because the consequences are severe, staff who continually fail to follow the well-defined and modeled rules may be terminated. When these essential policies are not adhered to, an operation can be cited during inspections, and customers can become sick or even die from contaminated food. As a result of these unfortunate events, the business may have its reputation tarnished or end up going out of business. When it comes to handwashing, managers are responsible for:

- Ensuring that food employees wash their hands, as required.

- Providing accessible, adequately maintained, designated handwashing sinks.

- Making sure that handwashing sinks have clean, running warm water, soap and paper towels, or other approved means for drying.

- Posting signage that notifies food employees of the handwashing requirement.

- Monitoring food employees to ensure proper handwashing and suitable hand hygiene protocol during the work shift.

FDA Handwashing Study

To help emphasize the challenges of complying with the Food Code, consider the surprising results of a study performed by the FDA in 2018. Full-service and fast-food restaurants were out of compliance with proper handwashing practices by 81% and 65%, respectively. That's right, less than half the time, hands are not being adequately cleaned to prevent cross-contamination, which can put customers at risk of serious illness. To improve handwashing compliance:

FDA Employee Health and Personal Hygiene Handbook, Page 16

Make it a Priority

Consistent enforcement of a mandatory handwashing policy will lead to greater compliance.

Remove Deterrents

Provide sinks near the needed areas and keep them clean and accessible. Make sure they are consistently stocked with soap, paper towels, and a trash can. The sink should also have warm water.

Motivate & Reward Staff

Recognize and reward compliance with the handwashing policy to motivate staff.

While this entire book is about food safety and culinary arts, this section will briefly introduce some essential topics to anyone who works with food in a commercial capacity must know. Basic food safety topics:

> Working with ready-to-eat (RTE) foods   Using single-use gloves

> Understanding rules related to employee illness and disease   Wearing hair restraints

Ready-to-Eat (RTE) Foods

Any food that can be eaten as-is and does not need to be washed to remove germs or if it has already been cooked is considered a ready-to-eat (RTE) food. Examples of RTE foods include:

- Any food not cooked after final preparation, such as sushi or sandwiches
- Washed produce that is eaten raw, such as fruits and salads
- Bakery or bread items, such as toast or rolls
- Cooked food, such as pizza and hamburgers
- Garnishes, like parsley, lemon wedges, or pickles on plates
- Fruits or vegetables for mixed drinks or smoothies
- Ice

Never handle RTE foods with bare hands!

3-301.11

An essential rule is to never handle ready-to-eat foods with bare hands (with rare exceptions in some jurisdictions). However, it is acceptable to handle RTE foods if there is a subsequent pathogen-kill step. For example, it is OK to use bare hands to add cooked bacon as an ingredient to a dish that will be cooked (to a minimum internal temperature specified in the FDA Food Code). Another example, which is allowed, is using bare hands to add cheese topping to a pizza. In these scenarios, any pathogens which may have transferred from the food employee's hands to the food will be destroyed or reduced to safe levels. By contrast, it is not acceptable to add a cheese topping to a sandwich with bare hands.

Even with effective handwashing practices, heavily contaminated hands can still transmit pathogens from bare hands to food and contribute to a foodborne illness outbreak. Therefore, RTE foods must be handled with suitable utensils. Utensils to handle ready-to-eat foods include:

- Deli paper
- Tongs
- Spatula

- Single-use gloves
- Chopsticks
- Toothpicks

- Scoops
- Ladles
- Other utensils

Protective Coverings

In addition to good personal hygiene, a food employee must wear proper protective coverings, as required, when working with food or food equipment. This section will cover the "what" and the "when" requirements for protective coverings to prevent food contamination.

Single-use Gloves

Combined with proper hand washing, using single-use gloves when handling RTE foods can effectively decrease the transfer of pathogens from hands to food and thus minimize the chances of a foodborne illness outbreak. It is essential, however, to keep in mind that the use of suitable gloves does not guarantee protection from the transmission of microorganisms from hands to food. Therefore, the best course of action is staff training on handwashing and glove usage, followed by consistent modeling and enforcement.

Figure 5

Follow these instructions for the use of single-use gloves:

- Wash hands before using gloves

2-304.15(A)

- Change gloves and wash hands between handling RTE foods, raw ingredients, or when interruptions in a workflow happen

- Do not reuse or wash disposable or single-use gloves

- Discard damaged or torn single-use gloves

Annex 3, 4-602.11

- Gloves are considered utensils, and as such must be replaced no less than every four hours during continued use to prevent the growth of pathogens.

- Wear single-use gloves over nail polish, artificial nails, or uncleanable orthopedic support devices.

If gloves are not used properly, they can become a source of cross-contamination. Since gloves are not put on the hands by someone else like they are for a surgeon, it is not hard to imagine how dirty hands can instantly contaminate the gloves while they are being put on. This contamination risk is why washing hands before using gloves is essential.

Annex 3, 3-304.15

2-304.15(D)

Latex can cause an allergic reaction to some staff and, in rare cases, customers consuming food touched by latex gloves. Cloth gloves, sometimes used by servers in fine dining establishments, may only touch food if it is subsequently cooked. Gloves should be purchased from an approved reputable vendor, and a latex alternative should be available for staff sensitive to latex. Since hands are not the same size, multiple glove sizes should be available for a correct fit, which helps with agility and safety while handling food.

2-201.11(A)(1)(2)(iii)

A cut, burn, or lesion containing pus such as a boil or infected wound that is open or draining must be covered by a dry, durable, tight-fitting bandage or finger cot. To help avoid contaminating food, bandages should be brightly colored and covered with a single-use glove.

2-401.13

Hair Restraints

2-402.11

To keep hair from touching or contaminating food, the Food Code requires that food employees wear hair restraints, such as nets, hats, and clothing covering body hair. This requirement does not apply to staff who only serve beverages and packaged or wrapped foods. Servers, hosts, and bus staff are also excluded from covering hair if they present minimal risk of contaminating exposed food, equipment, or utensils.

Figure 6

Personal Eating and Drinking

There are certain rules that must be followed related to a food employee consuming food or a beverage while working. The main goal of these rules is to prevent the contamination of food being prepared for the consumer.

Contained Beverages

It is essential to stay hydrated while working as a food employee to stay healthy and work efficiently. Staff often drink water or soda throughout their shift—water is better for keeping hydrated. While consuming a beverage is allowed, even in the work area, there are some rules to follow to prevent direct or cross-contamination of food. Beverage rules for food staff:

- Closed container; *with lid and straw or sip lid*
- Stored on a non-food contact surface; e.g., *a supply shelf or atop a microwave*
- Separate from exposed food, clean equipment, or unwrapped single-use articles

2-401.11

Eating and Tasting Food

When food must be taste-tested to ensure proper seasoning, the utensil may only be used once to prevent food contamination. Corrective action must be taken immediately when food employees are out of compliance. This involves disposing of contaminated food, cleaning affected equipment, and retraining.

Food workers are not allowed to eat meals in or around food preparation or production areas. Instead, they must eat in a breakroom, the dining room, or outside of the operation.

2-401.11
6-403.11

An inspection by the local authority (health inspector) can cite the restaurant as **"out of compliance"** if a food employee is **observed** eating in non-designated areas or drinking from a non-enclosed cup. This is also true if **evidence** of a Food Code violation is revealed during an inspection, such as a cup without a lid, a cup found sitting on a food-contact surface, or a plate of partially eaten food discovered in a food preparation area.

Staff Health– Related Issues

2-201.11

The personal health of people who work with food is not entirely private due to the potential of contaminating food and the related danger to the consumer from foodborne illness. Even before symptoms occur, an illness can be contagious and infect co-workers or contaminate food and equipment. Food employees are considered a **carrier** when they have a virus or disease that can spread through food. Because of this, the FDA Food Code requires employees to sign a form agreeing to **inform management** when they have specific symptoms, whether at work or not.

The following symptoms must be reported, including the date the symptoms were first experienced:

- Vomiting
- Diarrhea
- Sore throat with fever
- Jaundice
- Infected cuts, wounds, or lesions containing pus on exposed body parts

When these symptoms occur before arriving to work, staff must not report to work. Instead, they are to call or text their manager. When these symptoms are reported or observed during a shift, the manager will **exclude** or **restrict** the employee following the FDA Decision Tree (Figure 7). In the case of exclusion, the food employee will not be allowed to return to work for at least 24 hours after the symptoms have occurred.

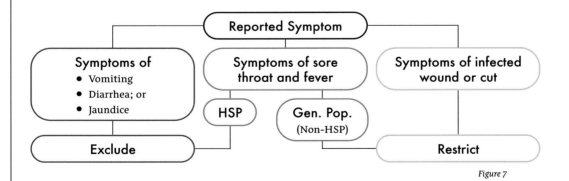

Figure 7

Highly Susceptible Population

People who are immunocompromised or receive food at healthcare or day-care-type facilities are considered a highly susceptible population (HPS). This high-risk population includes preschool-aged children, older adults, and anyone with certain underlying health conditions. Because this group of consumers is more likely to experience foodborne illness, including more intense symptoms and a higher mortality rate, they are carefully considered in the FDA Food Code and throughout this book. As a result, certain foods and practices are prohibited when a food establishment exclusively serves HPS consumers (i.e., not the general population) in a nursing home, for example. Do not offer for sale or serve these foods in a ready-to-eat form:

- Raw animal foods, including raw marinated fish, raw molluscan shellfish, steak tartar
- Animal food not cooked to the minimum required temperatures, such as lightly-cooked fish, rare meat, soft-cooked shell eggs, and meringue
- Raw seed sprouts
- Unpasteurized juices

3-801.11

Exclusion and Restriction

It is helpful to understand the distinction between the two corrective actions taken by a manager or person in charge (PIC) related to personal health issues - namely, exclusion and restriction. First, understand that neither is a form of punishment but a health safety precaution. **Exclusion** means a food employee is not allowed to enter or work in a food establishment. **Restriction** limits a food employee, who has a risk of spreading a disease that is transmissible through food, from working with clean equipment, or exposed food. An exclusion or restriction applies to all food establishments. Staff must also report if diagnosed with the following disease or medical condition:

2-201.12

- Norovirus
- Hepatitis A
- Salmonella Typhi (Typhoid fever)
- Nontyphoidal Salmonella
- E. coli (or other STEC)
- Shigella spp. (Shigellosis)

Manager's Responsibility

Managers need to watch for signs of illness, such as Jaundice (yellowing of the skin or eyes), increased bathroom breaks, persistent sneezing, coughing, or signs of fever. When these symptoms are observed, the manager must discuss this with the employee and take corrective action as necessary.

2-401.12

With proper medical documentation, some non-infectious conditions do not affect an employee's ability to handle food safely. Examples are Crohn's disease, irritable bowel syndrome, and some liver diseases. The Americans with Disabilities Act (ADA) protects the right to work for individuals with infectious diseases not spread through food, such as HIV/AIDS, Hepatitis B, Hepatitis C, and Tuberculosis.

Summary

The theme of this chapter is how food employees can keep food safe from contamination. The main goal of safe food handling is to protect the consumer from foodborne illnesses caused by contaminated food. This is especially true for the highly susceptible population (HSP), who are more likely to experience foodborne illness and have a more severe, potentially fatal reaction due to their age or underlying health conditions. The preventative measures discussed in this chapter include maintaining good personal hygiene, properly washing hands, using protective coverings as required, and reporting any personal health issues. With proper training, monitoring, corrective action, and retraining, a food establishment significantly reduces the risks of a foodborne illness outbreak.

- The highly susceptible population (HSP) have a higher risk of experiencing foodborne illness due to age and health.

- Staff must arrive to work clean, well-groomed, and practice good personal hygiene.

- Corrective action involves intervening in an unsafe practice and retraining.

- A food handler is considered a carrier when they have a virus or disease that can spread through food.

- Ready-to-eat foods (RTE) can be eaten as-is and do not require subsequent or additional cooking. RTE examples include lettuce, bread, potato chips, and cake.

- Food employees must know how and when to wash their hands to reduce the chances of cross-contamination.

- Bright-colored bandages & single-use gloves must be used to avoid food contamination.

- Exclusion means a food employee is not allowed to enter or work in a food establishment, whereas restriction limits them from working with clean equipment or exposed food.

The Student's Workbook

As assigned by your instructor, use the separate Student's Workbook to work independently or in groups. Activities for this week's chapter include:

- Create a handwashing poster

- Vote on the best (and completely accurate) poster in the class

- Watch the video and reflect

- Discuss the risks of each ingredient in the Chef's Salad recipe

- Make a list of equipment needed

- Review the cleaning and sanitizing checklist

- Fill out the recipe and cost form

Review Questions

Use these questions to check your knowledge of the material in this chapter. *Your instructor has the answers.*

1 Properly washing hands is an example of good _____.

a. attitude
b. hygiene
c. ethics
d. timing

2 The only jewelry allowed to be worn by a food handler is/are _____.

a. a simple wedding band
b. decorative rings
c. a medical bracelet
d. a decorative bracelet

3 Which is not one of the 5 steps of proper handwashing?

a. Rub hands together
b. Thorough drying
c. Use antiseptic
d. Wet hands

4 When working with ready-to-eat (RTE) foods, food handlers must use _____.

a. bare hands
b. colorful ingredients
c. single-use gloves
d. a flat surface

5 Hands should be washed in _____.

a. a handwashing sink
b. any sink
c. a mop sink
d. a bathroom

6 Corrective action includes _____.

a. addressing the issue at a later time
b. only scheduling retraining
c. adding more seasoning to a dish
d. an immediate response

7 Single-use gloves are not required when _____.

a. working with RTE foods
b. wearing artificial nails
c. working with raw meat
d. an uncleanable orthopedic device

8 A food employee who is vomiting must be _____.

a. restricted
b. excluded
c. retained
d. given extra breaks

Chapter 03
Bad Bugs

The world is filled with microorganisms, many of which are helpful to our health and the complex ecosystem surrounding us. However, some "bad bugs" (or pathogens) are harmful to human health and need to be avoided or managed and kept to safe levels. Good personal hygiene, covered in the previous chapter, is how people protect themselves from getting sick from bad bugs, such as washing hands often (especially after using the toilet), wearing clean clothes, and personal grooming.

In the foodservice industry, understanding and managing "bad bugs" is a serious matter since the health of others, i.e., the consumer or the public, is at stake. There are many ways dangerous pathogens can enter food and cause foodborne illness when consumed. For example, food can arrive contaminated, it can become contaminated by poor food handling, and it can become contaminated by food employees who are sick while they work or do not practice good personal hygiene. Proper training and application paired with consistent corrective action are crucial to preventing foodborne illness or an outbreak involving two or more people.

Key Terms

Keep an eye out for these essential topics:

- Pathogens
- Bacteria
- FAT TOM
- Virus
- Spore

- Toxins
- Parasite
- Fungi

Objectives

After working through this chapter, you should be able to explain the following to friends and family:

- Describe the Big 6 pathogens
- Know the non-living entities: viruses, spores, and toxins
- Explain the symptoms associated with the Big 6

- Know the living pathogens: bacteria, fungi, and parasites
- Understand how FAT TOM relates to bacterial growth
- Know that some pathogens cannot be destroyed by cooking

Russell,
Executive Chef

Russell was recently promoted to Executive Chef of a fine-dining seafood restaurant in Boulder City, NV, not far from Lake Mead and the famous Hoover Dam. After two months, he was struggling — not with the food or menu offerings, and the customers were delighted. It was the owner, Cedric, who was unhappy. The restaurant, under his management, was not making enough money. Something must change with a drastic reduction in food costs. Otherwise, the owner would switch to another executive chef!

Concerned with this dilemma, Russell pondered what options he had. Being four hours from the Pacific Ocean, fresh seafood would be expensive. If he bought frozen seafood, it could be cheaper but often sourced from other regions like China or Vietnam, but this was not a viable option for a fine-dining restaurant. He had to do something and fast.

The following day, all his concerns melted away when there was a knock on the kitchen's back door. Louis, a 25-year-old self-proclaimed entrepreneur, had an offer that seemed to be the perfect answer. Louis and his best friend Jaquavis were avid fishermen. They were successfully pulling 30+ pounds of fish from Lake Mead every day. All Louis wanted was fuel for his boat and bait. That way, he and Jaquavis could continue their favorite pastime, fishing. With a simple handshake, the deal was done, and Russell felt his concerns would soon be behind him.

The following day, shortly before lunchtime, Louis knocked on the kitchen's back door with a big grin and 15 pounds of striped bass, 8 pounds of rainbow trout, and 14 pounds of catfish. Russell quickly put it all in the refrigerator, on ice, in a drip pan. Life was looking good!

The fish was prepped up for a busy dinner service, and Russell was excited with their fish specials out selling every other menu option combined. At 7:45 pm, everything would change. A lady at table 12 started complaining of what looked like an allergic reaction. Benadryl (an anti-histamine) seemed to help her. But that was just the start, and it all seemed to snowball quickly. Table after table had similar complaints, headaches, reddening in their face and necks. Quite a few had to go to the restrooms, and things got messy! The maitre d' demanded Russell go and speak with the customers before a riot broke out.

Scombroid poisoning from histamine toxins in fish has a fast reaction, affecting the body, sometimes appearing as an allergic reaction, but also causing headaches, neurological issues, vomiting, and diarrhea. Unlike other pathogens we study that can take many hours to affect the body, histamine can start causing symptoms in minutes. The usual Time and Temperature control are essential, but Reputable Approved Suppliers are key.

References in this Coursebook:

Glossary reference: Orange text means the definition of the word can be found in the Glossary located in the Student Workbook.

Food Code section reference: To verify or further study topics covered in this Coursebook, the FDA Food Code section numbers are provided in the margins. The current version of the offical code may be download here:
https://www.fda.gov/food/retail-food-protection/fda-food-code

Introduction

The cooking of food, the storage of food, and the food itself make food a chemically complex topic. This chapter will explore fundamental principles every food handler needs to know to do their part in keeping food safe from biological hazards or "bad bugs."

WHAT IS A BAD BUG? A microorganism or naturally occurring contaminant that, at certain levels of concentration, cause foodborne illness in consumed food.

"Bad bugs" range from live pathogenic organisms, such as bacteria, fungi, and parasites, to non-living entities, such as viruses, spores, and natural toxins. This book will often refer to these collectively as pathogens.

Of the over 40 pathogens leading to foodborne illness, the Food and Drug Administration (FDA) and Centers for Disease Control (CDC) name six that are highly infective and easily transmitted by food employees. These Big 6 pathogens have a low infectious dose, contaminate the gastrointestinal system after ingestion, and shed in feces in high numbers. A food employee infected with a Big 6 pathogen typically sheds hundreds of thousands of pathogens in their feces that can be easily transmitted to food even when using good handwashing practices.

BAD BUGS	
Living	Non-Living
Bacteria	Viruses
Fungi	Spores
Parasites	Toxins

THE BIG 6	
Hepatitis A	Virus
Norovirus	Virus
Salmonella spp. (nontyphoidal)	Bacteria
Salmonella Typhi (typhoid-like fever)	Bacteria
Shiga toxin-producing Escherichia coli (E. coli)	Toxin
Shigella spp. (causes shigellosis)	Bacteria

Concept reinforcement: A combination of three interventions covered in the previous chapter can effectively limit the transmission of foodborne viruses and bacteria in food establishments.

These interventions include:

- Restricting or excluding food employees from working with food when sick
- Employing correct handwashing procedures
- Eliminating bare hand contact with ready-to-eat (RTE) foods

Managers enforcing each intervention will help prevent the transmission of pathogens from food employees to consumers through contaminated food.

The following two sections will look at the six types of bag bugs, both living and non-living. They don't have to be groups based on living or not; it is done more as a memory device.

Living Organisms

With a focus on how they relate to food and can negatively affect human health, this section will define three living organisms essential to understand: bacteria, fungi, and parasites.

Figures 1-3

Bacteria   *Fungi*   *Parasites*

Bacteria

Bacteria is a common foodborne contaminant made up of a single cell. Most bacteria are not harmful, but some can cause illness when ingested, usually with food. Another source of foodborne illness is spores and toxins produced by bacteria, which are covered later in this chapter.

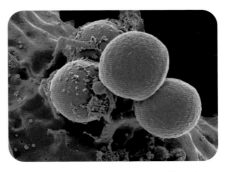

Figure 4

Bad bugs bacteria:

- **Salmonella spp.** (nontyphoidal)
- **Salmonella Typhi** (typhoid-like fever)
- Campylobacter jejuni
- **Shigella spp.**
- Clostridium perfringens
- Clostridium botulinum
- Staphylococcus aureus
- Streptococcus spp.
- Bacillus cereus
- Listeria monocytogenes
- Vibrio vulnificus
- Vibrio parahaemolyticus

Figure 4

Understanding the intrinsic and extrinsic factors that encourage, prevent, or limit bacterial growth is essential food handler knowledge. Bacterial growth describes the number, not size, of bacteria as they grow by splitting into two cells. Not surprisingly, most foods contain sufficient nutrients to support bacterial growth. Fundamental bacterial growth factors:

- Intrinsic: Inherent to food, such as additives or pH level.
- Extrinsic: External conditions under which food is stored, such as temperature and moisture or oxygen levels.

> The use of anti-bacterial soap is one of the reasons handwashing is effective at reducing foodborne illness.

FAT TOM

The mnemonic device FAT TOM is used to describe conditions affecting the growth rate of bacteria. Understanding and controlling these six intrinsic and extrinsic factors greatly reduce the potential of foodborne contamination and consumer illness.

Figure 5

Food

Like all living things, bacteria need a source of food such as proteins and carbohydrates (an intrinsic factor of food) to survive. Some foods support the growth of bacteria more than others, especially if the extrinsic factors of time and temperature are abused. These foods are referred to as TCS Foods (Time/Temperature Control for Safety Foods); examples are eggs, dairy products, and meats.

Acidity

The pH value of food, which is a measurement of acidity, is based on the following scale:

- 0.0 Highly acidic
- 7.0 Neutral
- 14.0 Highly alkaline

Bacterial growth is optimal in foods with little or no acidity (pH 7.5–4.6). Microbial growth is slowed when the pH is adjusted in either direction from this optimal range. For example, foods with high acidity or when used as an ingredient help limit bacterial growth (below 4.5 pH). Examples of foods with high acidity or low pH levels are:

- Limes: 1.8–2.4
- Vinegar: 2.0–3.4
- Cranberries: 2.3–2.5

Temperature

Like pH levels, temperature values for bacterial growth have a minimum and maximum range, outside of which growth is limited. This range, called the temperature danger zone, is 41°F–135°F (5°C–57°C). Bacterial growth potential is highest when food is between 70°F–125°F (21°C–52°C).

Time

Time is necessary for bacterial growth, especially within the temperature danger zone. If food is held at improper temperatures for enough time, bacteria can multiply to dangerous levels. Many foods require active cooling methods to cool quickly enough to limit the growth of bacteria that can lead to foodborne illness.

Oxygen

Bacterial growth usually requires oxygen, but not always. In canned goods containing contaminants, bacteria can grow in low oxygen conditions. Certain bacteria can grow without oxygen in cooked rice and time-temperature abused baked potatoes.

Moisture (a_w)

The moisture content in food can contribute to bacterial growth. However, we are most interested in Water Activity (a_w) levels, not moisture content, when considering food safety. Water Activity is measured on a scale of 0-1.0. A solution of pure water is 1.0 a_w, which decreases as other substances are added. Conditions are ideal for bacterial growth when at or above 0.85a_w. Some bacteria survive on low-moisture foods such as spices (e.g., black pepper, 0.4a_w) and infant baby powder.

There are four phases of bacterial growth: slow growth (lag-phase), Rapid growth (log-phase), equilibrium (stationary-phase), and reduction (death-phase). Following the blue line in the graph, notice that rapid growth occurs within the temperature danger zone, where bacteria can double in as little as 20 minutes. Once food reaches its minimum internal temperature, bacteria begin to die quickly.

Refrigeration is an important food safety control point as it can limit the growth of most foodborne bacteria, holding them at low levels safe for consumption. The development of most bacteria is limited at temperatures of 40°F (4°C) and lower. Just one degree higher, and bacteria thrive within the temperature danger zone.

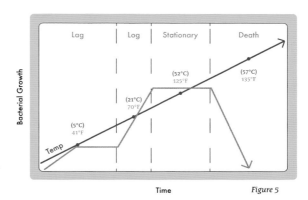

Figure 5

Annex 3, Page 118

As important as refrigeration is, there are good reasons not to count on it as your only food-safety measure, according to the CDC. A few bacteria can multiply at refrigeration temperatures and even at average home-freezer temperatures. Thus, cooking to a food's minimum internal temperature becomes an important pathogen-kill step in keeping food safe for consumption.

The key to controlling bacterial growth is understanding and managing FAT TOM conditions. **Bacteria-preventative measures include:**

- **Storage**: packaged or sealed food at the proper temperature (see chapter 7)
- **Cooking**: reaching a minimum temperature (see chapter 8)
- **Holding**: keeping service food out of the danger zone (see chapter 9)

Fungi

The presence of fungi (i.e., mushrooms, molds, and yeasts) is widespread in the air, ground, and some foods. Certain fungi are safe to eat, while others are the most dangerous due to naturally occurring toxins. Additionally, yeasts and molds can shift the food pH, promoting bacterial growth. The potential foodborne dangers associated with fungi make it an essential topic for food employees to understand.

KEY TERM Poison is a chemical substance that can cause foodborne illness when consumed.

KEY TERM Toxins are poisons made by living things, such as fungi, before or after consumption.

Mushrooms

Certain mushrooms contain toxins that cause foodborne illness. These mushrooms are nearly impossible to distinguish from non-poisonous varieties and can cause mild to severe symptoms. Moreover, the poison is rarely destroyed by washing, cooking, freezing, or canning. A consumer can get sick from eating a sauce that contains the mushrooms while not eating the mushroom directly.

Annex 3, Page 81

> According to the FDA, over 5000 species of fleshy mushrooms grow naturally in North America. Although most have never been tested for toxicity, what we do know is:
>
> **15** species are deadly
>
> **36** species are suspected of being poisonous (raw or cooked)
>
> **60** species are toxic to humans (raw or cooked)
>
> **40** other species are poisonous if eaten raw, but are safe after proper cooking

The symptoms from some of the deadliest mushrooms can be delayed for hours, days, or even weeks. By the time symptoms occur, there can be severe organ damage. The most severe cases of psilocybin poisoning, mushrooms that cause neurological problems, occur in small children, where large doses can cause fever, hallucinations, and death.

3-201.16

The best preventative measure is only to buy mushrooms from an approved reputable distributor. The FDA Food Code does not allow wild mushrooms to be offered for sale or service by a food establishment.

Mold

Molds are spores produced by fungi that live on plant or animal matter. Unlike one-celled bacteria, molds are made of many cells and can sometimes be seen without a microscope. The spores can be transported by air, water, or insects.

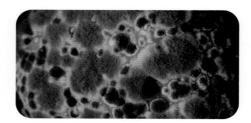

Figure 5

Molds can thrive within a wide range of environmental conditions, such as:

- pH: 2–9

- Temperature: 50°F–95°F (10°C–35°C)

- Water activity: 0.85 a$_w$ or lower

Molds grow well in jellies, jams, and bacon and ham (i.e., cured meats), which have low water activity and are acidic.

Some food molds are safe to eat, such as the white surface mold on brie and camembert cheeses. Additionally, the USDA allows some foods, e.g., hard cheeses and firm fruits, to be consumed after cutting off naturally occurring surface mold-removing at least 1" (25mm) around and below the mold.

USDA, Molds on Food: Are They Dangerous

Several foodborne molds may be hazardous when consumed because of their ability to produce mycotoxins, which can make consumers sick or cause an allergic reaction. For example, **aflatoxin** is a toxin produced by mold and associated with the following foods:

- corn and corn products

- peanuts and peanut products

- cottonseed, milk, and tree nuts such as Brazil nuts

- pecans, pistachio nuts, and walnuts

Annex 4, Page 13

Other grains and nuts are susceptible but less prone to contamination. See chapter 4 for more on allergens.

> **KEY TERM** The USDA defines Mycotoxins as poisonous substances produced by certain molds found primarily in grain and nut crops, but are also known to be on celery, grape juice, apples, and other produce. There are many of them and scientists are continually discovering new ones. The Food and Agriculture Organization (FAO) of the United Nations estimates that 25% of the world's food crops are affected by mycotoxins, of which the most notorious are aflatoxins.

Beyond food contamination, there are other mold-related concerns to be mindful of within a food operation. For example, molds allowed to form on the drain lines of an ice machine are difficult to remove and present a risk of cross-contamination to the ice stored in the bin. Following a routine cleaning and sanitization schedule will significantly reduce the chances of dangerous mold levels accumulating.

Annex 3, Page 163

Mold-preventative measures include:

- When serving food, keep it covered to prevent exposure to mold spores in the air. Use plastic wrap to cover foods you want to stay moist—fresh or cut fruits and vegetables, and green and mixed salads.
- Empty opened cans of perishable foods into clean storage containers and refrigerate them promptly.
- Foods delivered with visible signs of mold should be rejected. Chapter 6
- Routinely clean and sanitize equipment to prevent mold growth. Chapters 10 and 11

4-602.11(E)(4)(b)

Yeasts

Yeasts are single-celled microorganisms, with over 1,500 species documented, which are a form of fungi. Some yeasts are used safely as an ingredient in food preparation. For example, yeast is a leavening agent that causes bread to rise. It is also used to promote fermentation in the production of beer and wine.

Annex 3, Page 157

However, some species of yeast can cause infection in people; the most common is Candida albicans, according to the CDC. Candida usually lives on the skin and inside the body without causing problems. Candida can cause infections if it grows out of control or enters deep into the body. For example, it can cause infections in the bloodstream or internal organs like the kidney, heart, or brain. Yeast has also been linked to Salmonella illness.

As previously mentioned, water activity is important because it can be used to predict the growth of harmful bacteria, yeasts, and molds. Food products with low water activity will last longer on the shelf because they do not provide a good environment for pathogens to grow. Some foods where yeast growth is optimal may not require refrigeration because they have a combination of an acidic pH and low water activity. Examples include jams, jellies, honey, and syrup.

Figure 6

Preventative measures in a food operation include visual inspection of delivered and stored food. Food should be rejected or discarded when signs of spoilage are observed, like white specks or bubbles on the surface.

Parasites

Parasites are organisms that derive protection and nourishment from a host (human or animal) in a way that is of no advantage to the host or harms it by restricting normal organ functions or robbing nutrients. They range in size, from tiny single-celled organisms to worms visible to the naked eye. Parasites do not grow in food but can be transmitted through it.

Parasitic Protozoa and Worms

Toxoplasmosis gondii
Giardia lamblia
Entamoeba histolytica
Cryptosporidium parvum
Cyclospora cayetanensis

Annex 3, Page 105

There are three ways parasites usually enter the food chain. These include:

- Direct contamination of food ingredients or farm-fresh produce
- Contaminated water sources used in irrigation, washing, or processing foods
- Direct human transfer by food handlers

From the FDA Food Code:

Parasitic infections are commonly associated with undercooking meat products or cross-contamination of ready-to-eat food with raw animal foods, untreated water, or contaminated equipment or utensils. Like viruses, parasites do not grow in food, so control is focused on destroying the parasites and/or preventing their introduction. Adequate cooking destroys parasites. In addition, parasites in fish to be consumed raw or undercooked can also be destroyed by effective freezing techniques.

Annex 4, Page 7

Parasites-preventative measures include:

- Use an approved, reputable distributor
- Cook to minimum temperatures
- Freeze fish properly if served raw or undercooked
- No bare hand contact with ready-to-eat foods
- Proper handwashing
- Restriction or exclusion of ill employees
- Prevention of cross-contamination

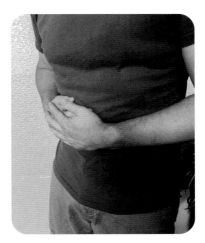

Annex 3, Page 110

Figure 7

Non-living Entities

With a focus on how they relate to food and can negatively affect human health, this section will define three non-living entities essential to understand: viruses, spores, and toxins.

Figures 8-10

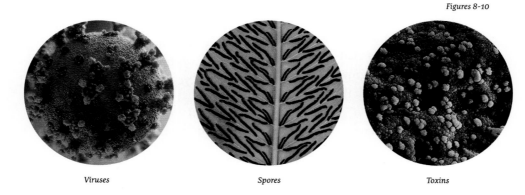

Viruses   Spores   Toxins

Viruses

Unlike bacteria, viruses are not living organisms but are essentially DNA or RNA covered by protein. Viruses are not able to reproduce on their own. Instead, they multiply in a host rather than growing, technically. A virus enters the cells of other living things, including humans, and appropriates those cellular substances to multiply itself. The virus can mass produce copies of itself in this way.

As the name implies, the Coronavirus (a.k.a., COVID-19) is a virus. Although there is currently no evidence to support the transmission of COVID-19 associated with food, public awareness of how viruses behave, in general, increased significantly during the global pandemic. For example, depending on the surface type, viruses can exist for hours to days before breaking down and becoming inactive. Notably, washing hands properly for 10—15 seconds to give the handsoap time to neutralize the virus is essential to prevent self-infection or cross-contamination.

Viruses
Noroviruses
Hepatitis A
Hepatitis E
Rotavirus

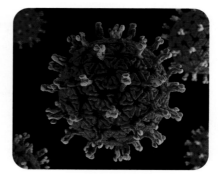

Figure 11

Norovirus

Norovirus is a very contagious virus that causes vomiting and diarrhea. It is the leading cause of illness from contaminated food or water in the U.S. Anyone can get infected and sick with norovirus. You can get norovirus from:

- Having direct contact with an infected person
- Consuming contaminated food or water
- Touching contaminated surfaces and putting your unwashed hands in your mouth

Norovirus infections are associated with the consumption of ready-to-eat (RTE) food contaminated by food handlers, the environmental contamination of produce, or the consumption of molluscan shellfish harvested from contaminated water. In each group, transmission occurs through the **fecal-oral route** (or vomit, occasionally) and is often associated with improper personal hygiene, health, and food operation sanitation.

Annex 3, Page 20

> Unlike bacteria, which thrive in the temperature danger zone, norovirus is most stable at cool storage temperatures.

Symptoms usually start within 1 or 2 days of consuming contaminated food but may begin in just 12 hours. The first symptoms are often explosive vomiting and watery diarrhea that isn't bloody. Headache, cramps, a mild fever, and muscle aches also may occur. Most people recover in 1-2 days. Occasionally, some people lose so much body fluid they need to be treated by a health professional and are hospitalized in some cases. Antibiotics don't work against this or other viruses; they only work against bacteria.

Norovirus-preventative measures include:

- Proper hand washing practices
- Rinse fruits and vegetables
- Cook shellfish thoroughly
- Exclude sick workers experiencing jaundice, diarrhea, or vomiting

2-201.13(A)(2)

Figure 12

Spores

Some bacteria create spores (a.k.a., endospores) as a survival mechanism that are not destroyed by cooking, freezing, refrigeration, or sanitation at lower concentrations. Their rugged protection against harsh environments allows them to exist for many years with little-to-no nutrition available. When conditions improve, e.g., finding their way into food through cross-contamination, the spores become active bacteria again. These newly formed bacteria have their growth limited or are reduced/destroyed to safe levels by cooking, refrigeration, and freezing in most cases, as previously discussed in this chapter.

The particularly rugged **C. perfringens** spores can survive cooking and hot holding. If food is time-temperature abused, spores can germinate to become rapidly multiplying vegetative cells (bacteria).

Annex 4, Page 6

According to the FDA Food Code:

The toxins produced by the vegetative cells of Bacillus cereus, Clostridium botulinum, and Staphylococcus aureus may not be destroyed to safe levels by reheating. Post-cook recontamination with vegetative cells of bacteria such as Salmonellae and Campylobacter jejuni is also a major concern for operators of retail and food service establishments.

Annex 3, Page 112

Cooked food should be cooled rapidly to prevent the growth and multiplication of spore-forming organisms. Spores can germinate when food spends too much time in the temperature danger zone, and the resultant bacteria can multiply to dangerous levels. Additionally, harmful toxins may be produced in the presence of sufficient numbers of **C. botulinum** or other spore-forming organisms. Therefore, ensuring no growth of these organisms will provide the most significant amount of safety.

Spores-preventative measures include:

- Properly wash hands
- Prevent cross-contamination
- Cool cooked foods quickly
- Cook foods to minimum internal temperatures

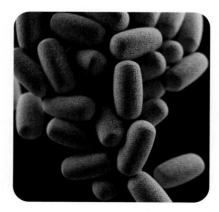

Figure 13

Toxins

A toxin is a poison created by a living organism but is a non-living substance. Dangerous toxins exist in some mushrooms, fish, and shellfish. Additionally, some animals have toxins in the form of venom. Several foodborne molds may be hazardous when consumed because of their ability to produce mycotoxins. Toxins can also be made in foods by certain bacteria, such as the enterotoxins of *Staphylococcus aureus*.

Shiga toxin-producing *Escherichia coli* (STEC) is one of the "Big 6" foodborne causing illnesses. Restated, STEC is any E. coli bacteria capable of producing the harmful Shiga toxin. When consumed, symptoms range from asymptomatic, to non-bloody/bloody stools, to kidney failure.

These poisons are rarely destroyed by washing, cooking, freezing, or canning. Bacterial growth and toxin production are also possible through improper thawing, where a food spends too much time in the temperature danger zone.

Toxins-preventative measures include:

- Buy from an approved reputable distributor
- Avoid time-temperature abuse

Natural Toxins

Shiga
Ciguatoxin
Shellfish toxins
(PSP, DSP, NSP, ASP, AZP)
Scombrotoxin
Tetrodotoxin
Mushroom toxins
Aflatoxins
Gempylotoxin
Pyrrolizidine alkaloids
Venomous fish
Grayanotoxins
Phytohaemagglutinin

Annex 3, Page 129

Bad Bug Symptoms

How foodborne illness can be avoided varies depending on the type of food and the pathogen involved. Similarly, the time it takes for symptoms to present, what symptoms are experienced, and how long they last also vary greatly. Although it is a lot of information, it is helpful to understand. This information may be included on the certification exam, so be sure to spend time reviewing it.

Causative Pathogen	Incubation Time	Length of Illness	Common Symptoms	
Bacillus cereus	1 - 16 hours	6 - 24 hours	nausea, vomiting, cramping, diarrhea	
Campylobacter	2 - 5 days	1 - 4 days	cramping, fever, diarrhea, nausea, headache, vomiting	
Clostridium perfringens	8 - 24 hours	24 - 36 hours	abdominal cramping, diarrhea, nausea	
Shiga Toxin-producing E. coli	12 - 72 hours	1 - 4 days	diarrhea- often bloody, severe cramping, nausea, vomiting, fever	
Hepatitis A	10 - 50 days	1 - 2 weeks *severe cases may last several months*	mild or no symptoms, then sudden onset of fever, general discomfort, fatigue, headache, nausea, loss of appetite, vomiting, abdominal pain and jaundice after several days	
Listeria monocytogens	1 day - 3 weeks	Indefinite, *depends on treatment*	nausea, vomiting, fever, chills, headache, meningitis, miscarriages	
Norovirus	24- 48 hours	1 - 2 days	cramping, diarrhea, nausea, vomiting, headache, fever	
(Staph) Staphylococcus aureus	1 - 7 hours	1 - 2 days	onset abrupt and often severe, nausea, vomiting, cramping, sometimes diarrhea	
Non Typhoidal Salmonella	6 - 72 hours	1 - 3 days	abdominal cramping, headache, nausea, diarrhea, fever, sometimes vomiting	
Salmonella Typhi	6 - 30 days	2 - 4 weeks	Nausea, vomiting, cramps, diarrhea, fever & headaches	
Shigella	12 hours - 7 days	4 - 7 days *depends on treatment*	diarrhea- often bloody, cramping, fever, nausea, sometimes vomiting	

	Foods Involved / Sources	Prevention
	rice and rice dishes	cook to proper temp. reheat quickly. cool foods rapidly
	unpasteurized dairy, poultry and meats, infected food handler	thoroughly cook all foods. use only pasteurized dairy products. proper hand washing.
	meats, poultry, gravy, beans, stews, foods cooked slowly	cook and reheat foods to proper temp. cook in small batches. cool foods rapidly.
	raw and undercooked ground meats (esp. ground beef)	thoroughly cook ground meats. avoid cross-contamination.
	water, ice, shellfish, salads, cold cuts, sandwiches, fruits, fruit juices, milk, milk products, vegetables, and foods that will not receive further heat treatment	obtain shellfish from approved sources. prevent cross-contamination from hands. ensure food handlers practice good hand washing and no bare hand contact.
	unpasteurized dairy, cheese, vegetables, seafood, poultry	use only pasteurized dairy products. cook properly. hold refrigerated for limited time.
	raw fruit, raw vegetables, prepared salads, raw shellfish	thoroughly cook foods. wash hands. use certified shellfish. no bare hand contact.
	ready-to-eat goods, i.e. sandwiches, salads, ham and other meats, potato salads, custards, warmed-over foods; often from infected food handler's cuts, throat, nose, and acne	practice good hand washing and hygiene. avoid contamination. reduce bare hand contact with food. exclude food handlers with cuts and lesions. rapidly cool foods.
	undercooked or raw meats, poultry and shell eggs, poultry and egg salads, egg custards and sauces, protein foods, pets and infected handlers	avoid cross-contamination. cool and refrigerate foods immediately. cook meats/poultry thoroughly. practice good hand washing.
	Fecal/oral route from food handlers' and other animals' intestinal tracts.	practice good hand washing and hygiene. Avoid contamination and cook foods to minimum internal temperatures. Eliminate bare hand contact with food.
	ready-to-eat foods associated with bare hand contact (salads, sandwiches, etc.) Source: humans (feces) and flies	practice good handwashing after using toilet. use approved water and foods. control flies. no bare hand contact.

Figure 12

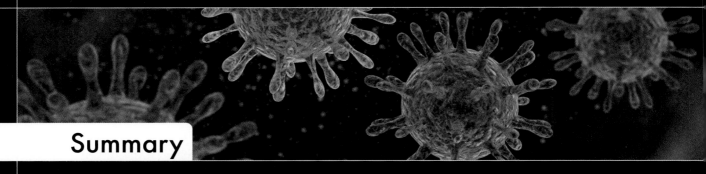

Summary

As stated at the beginning of the chapter, understanding and managing "bad bugs" is a serious matter since the health of others, i.e., the consumer or the public, is at stake. There are many ways dangerous pathogens can enter food and cause foodborne illness when consumed. For example, food can arrive contaminated, it can become contaminated by poor food handling, and it can become contaminated by food employees who are sick while they work or do not practice good personal hygiene. Proper training and application paired with consistent corrective action are crucial to preventing foodborne illness or an outbreak involving two or more people.

- The Big 6 pathogens: Hepatitis A, Norovirus, Salmonella spp., Salmonella Typhi, Shiga toxin-producing Escherichia coli, Shigella spp.

- Living pathogens grow in the right conditions: bacteria, fungi, and parasites

- Know the non-living entities that appropriate cells of a host: viruses, spores, and toxins

- FAT TOM stands for: Food, Acidity, Temperature, Time, Oxygen, and Moisture

- The symptoms associated with various pathogens are listed in the previous section.

- Poisons cannot be destroyed or made inactive by cooking.

The Student's Workbook

As assigned by your instructor, use the separate Student's Workbook to work independently or in groups. Activities for this week's chapter include:

- Create a FATTOM poster. Vote on the best (and completely accurate) poster in the class.

- Watch the video and reflect. Discuss the risks of each ingredient in the Meringue & Vacherin recipe.

- Make a list of equipment needed.

- Review the cleaning and sanitizing checklist.

- Make a presentation to your class on the results of the recipe.

Review Questions

se these questions to check your knowledge of the material in this chapter.
ur instructor has the answers.

1 Which is not a living pathogen?

a. bacteria

b. virus

c. parasites

d. fungi

2 Which is not one of the "Big 6" pathogens?

a. Hepatitis B

b. Salmonella Typhi

c. Shigella spp.

d. Hepatitis A

3 Which is an extrinsic condition of food?

a. pH level

b. additives

c. temperature

d. water activity

4 A neutral pH value is?

a. 0.0

b. 6.0

c. 7.0

d. 14.0

5 Water activity levels above _____ are ideal for bacterial growth.

a. $0.85a_w$

b. $0.01a_w$

c. $0.11a_w$

d. $0.95a_w$

6 Most bacterial growth is limited below this temperature:

a. 0°F (-18°C)

b. 32°F (0°C)

c. 45°F (7°C)

d. 40°F (4°C)

7 The norovirus is most stable around this temperature:

a. Arctic cold temperatures

b. hot oven temperatures

c. cool storage temperatures

d. any temperature

8 Natural toxins are not found in _____.

a. meat

b. mushrooms

c. fish

d. shellfish

Chapter 04

Food Hazards & Allergens

Introduction

Reading each chapter of this book by itself, you might think it is the most important chapter, given all the essential topics covered and the potential dangers to the consumer. However, food operations and the food itself are complicated, and the information found throughout this book must be understood and practiced concurrently to ensure food safety. This should not be discouraging, given it is accomplished every day worldwide. When these topics are tackled pragmatically and in a way that builds upon itself, the results are a fulfilling and rewarding career, not to mention loyal and satisfied customers. Achieving that result is one of the goals of this book.

This chapter covers food hazards, including physical, chemical, and allergens; biological hazards were covered in the previous chapter. Preventing these foodborne contaminants involves understanding cross-contact, cross-contamination, and intentional contamination. When a manager creates and maintains food safety and food defense programs the chances of consumers being harmed by foodborne illness are greatly reduced.

Key Terms

Keep an eye out for these essential topics:

- Allergens
- Adulterated food
- The Big 9
- ALERT
- Anaphylaxis
- FIRST
- Food defense
- Cross-contact
- Cross-contamination

Objectives

After working through this chapter, you should be able to explain the following to friends and family:

- Learn about the types of food contaminants
- Understand what cross-contamination is and how to prevent it
- Understand the types of thermometers and their uses
- Describe the flow of food
- Explain what TCS Foods are
- Know how to calibrate a bimetallic thermometer

Emily,
Supervisor

While she studied in high school, Emily enjoyed working part-time at the local French bistro. The interview was a breeze once she mentioned she had the Food Safety Manager certification. In her state, it is a legal requirement that the restaurant has at least one qualified individual on-site during all business operations.

Emily took this position seriously and was paid more than her colleagues. She was proud of her certification posted inside the restaurant for all to see. As a dining room supervisor, Emily would hold mini-training sessions with the staff each shift to keep them focused on safety. She had a good working relationship with the kitchen, too, as she knows it is impossible to be safe without excellent communication in the bistro.

One day this came into focus when a family of six entered the restaurant. They were celebrating the youngest daughter's sixteenth birthday and were quite demanding. Emily made sure to seat them in Alma's section, as she has an eye for detail and would wow them with her professionalism. While they placed their order, Emily overheard them mention that the youngest daughter had an acute allergy to sesame. Immediately this triggered her mind, not overdrive; safety first.

She checked in with Alma to see what the daughter had ordered: a simple grilled chicken salad. No problems with sesame there, as she breathed a sigh of relief. Just then, she noticed that hummus dip with pita chips had been ordered for the table as an appetizer. That's where Emily's training made the difference. Her first order of business was to educate the family about sesame paste in the hummus dip. They still wanted it but would ensure their daughter didn't eat it. Emily made sure at this point to inform Alma and the kitchen. Special care was taken to isolate the hummus from cross-contact issues with the salad, and Emily delivered the chicken to the young lady herself. Everyone enjoyed the celebration, and the night ended well. She thought to herself, knowing the BIG 9 made the difference, and she made the right call.

Introduction

There are many hazards to understand and monitor in a food operation to keep food employees and consumers safe.

Types of Contaminants

While the previous chapter covered several "bad bugs," it is helpful to remember that pathogens are not the only cause of foodborne contaminants. Here are the primary types of contaminants and a few specific examples of each:

Biological Hazards (Bad Bugs) *see chapter 3*
Bacteria, Viruses, Parasites, Yeast, Molds

Physical Hazards
Glass, Toothpicks, Fingernails, Jewelry

Chemical Hazards
Cleaners, Polishes, Sanitizers, Pesticides, Medications, First aid products, Metallic (elements/compounds)

Naturally Occurring Chemical Hazards
Fish toxins, Plant toxins

Allergen Hazards
The Big 9

Sources of Contaminants

Sources of these contaminants are primarily people and food:

Food employees
Contaminated hands, Illness

Foods
Contaminated food, Time and temperature abuse

Physical Hazards

Annex. 4, Page 17

Annex. 3, 2-401.13

A physical hazard is something in the food that is not meant for consumption and could cause injury or foodborne illness. Physical hazards include food packaging (e.g., labels, plastic wrap), jewelry (e.g., wedding ring, nose ring), bandages, and building materials (e.g., ceiling tile, wall paint, screws, and nails). Additionally, components of food that are not meant or prepared to be eaten (e.g., fruit rinds, pits, bone) fall into this category.

Materials of Concern

To better understand the sources and injury potential of foreign objects in food, Annex 4 of the FDA Food Code provides Table 4 (see Figure 1), titled **Main Materials of Concern as Physical Hazards and Common Sources**.

The potential serious injuries can include a patron fatally choking in the food operation. Such an event can cause irreparable harm to a business's reputation and lead to costly lawsuits. While these circumstances cannot be avoided entirely, well-trained and monitored staff can save people's lives. It is also highly recommended that some staff be trained in basic first aid, including the Heimlich maneuver, in case of a customer choking.

Material	Injury Potential	Sources
Glass fragments	Cuts, bleeding; *may require surgery to find or remove*	Bottles, jars, lights, utensils, gauge covers
Wood	Cuts, infection, choking; *may require surgery to remove*	Fields, pallets, boxes, buildings
Stones, metal fragments	Choking, broken teeth, cuts, and infection; *may require surgery to remove*	Fields, buildings, machinery, wire, employees
Insulation	Choking; *long-term if asbestos*	Building materials
Bone	Choking, trauma	Fields, improper plant processing
Plastic	Choking, cuts, infection; *may require surgery to remove*	Fields, plant packaging materials, pallets, employees
Personal Effects	Choking, cuts, broken teeth; *may require surgery to remove*	Employees—jewelry, earbuds, false eyelashes, etc.
Dirt, rocks	Choking, broken teeth, cuts, and infection; *may require surgery to remove*	Fields, wind, employees, raw dried beans

Annex. 4, Table 4

Annex. 3, 2-401.13

Figure 1

Preventative Measures

Physical hazard-preventative measures include:

- Personal hygiene
- Purchase from approved reputable distributors
- Delivery inspections
- Staff training and monitoring
- Follow facility cleaning and maintenance schedule

Chemical Hazards

The dangers of chemical hazards in a food operation are no trivial matter. There are many legitimate reasons to have dangerous chemical substances within a food operation; examples range from sanitation solutions to dish-washing machine detergents to pesticides. The dangers to human health include possible employee skin and eye contact and foodborne illnesses when contaminated foods are consumed.

Therefore, a strict **standard operating procedure** (SOP) must be implemented (see chapter 13) to ensure chemicals are used and stored correctly. These preventative measures include staff training, monitoring, corrective action, and retraining.

Special care should be taken not to contaminate foods, when cleaning in food preparation areas.

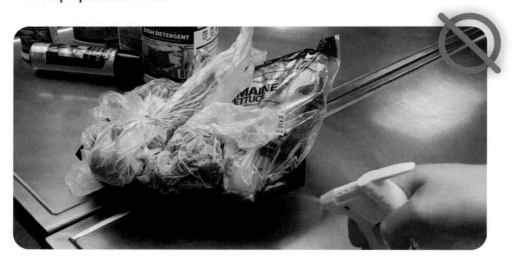

Figure 2

Materials of Concern

When mixed with tap water or highly acid foods, certain materials may create a dangerous chemical reaction that can cause food-borne illness. For example, some metals in the building construction, kitchen equipment, or utensils can present food hazards. Therefore, the FDA Food Code contains the following warnings and restrictions:

Figure 3

Pewter	*Found in: Water service vessels/pitchers*

The storage of acidic, moist foods such as orange juice or lemonade in pewter containers could result in food poisoning (heavy metal poisoning).

Annex 3, 4-101.13

Copper	*Found in: water pipes, pots, and pans*

High concentrations of copper are poisonous and have caused foodborne illness. When copper and copper alloy surfaces contact acidic foods, copper may be leached into the food. The building's plumbing components constructed of copper can cause, and have resulted in, the leaching of copper and lead into carbonated beverages.

Annex 3, 4-101.14

Zinc	*Found in: Stainless steel equipment and food contact surfaces*

Zinc is known to be toxic when ingested in large quantities. Under certain conditions, zinc may leach from galvanized food-contact surfaces into foods high in water content. The risk of leaching increases with the increased acidity of foods contacting the galvanized food-contact surface. Symptoms of zinc poisoning include vomiting, nausea, lethargy, fatigue, and epigastric pain. Most reports of zinc poisoning implicate contaminated food that resulted from storage in a galvanized metal container.

Annex 3, 4-101.15

To better understand the sources and control measures of naturally occurring chemical hazards in and around food, Annex 4 of the FDA Food Code provides Table 2b (see Figure 4), titled **Added Chemical Hazards at Retail, Along with Their Associated Foods and Control Measures**.

Symptoms include vomiting and diarrhea and can occur suddenly, after consuming contaminated food. It is essential to train staff on how to respond in an emergency, which includes calling 911 or the poison control center. The manager should have emergency numbers posted in the kitchen.

The FDA Food Code requires that poisonous or toxic materials be stored so they cannot contaminate food, equipment, utensils, linens, or single-use articles. Proper storage includes separating chemicals by space (i.e., distance) or partition (i.e., a separate room). Containers previously used for storing toxic chemicals cannot be used to store equipment, utensils, linens, single-service, or single-use articles. When separating by distance, the Food Code does not allow these materials to be stored above food or equipment.

7-203.11

Annex. 4, Table 2

Chemical Hazards	Associated Foods	Control Measures
Environmental contaminants: Pesticides, fungicides, fertilizers, insecticides, antibiotics, growth hormones	Any food may become contaminated.	Follow label instructions for use of environmental chemicals. Soil or water analysis may be used to verify safety.
PCBs	Fish	Comply with fish advisories.
Prohibited substances (21 CFR 189)	Numerous substances are prohibited from use in human food; no substance may be used in human food unless it meets all applicable requirements of the FD&C Act.	Do not use chemical substances that are not approved for use in human food.
Mercury	Fish exposed to organic mercury: shark, tilefish, king mackerel, and swordfish. Grains treated with mercury-based fungicides	Pregnant women/women of childbearing age/nursing mothers, and young children should not eat shark, swordfish, king mackerel or tilefish because they contain high levels of mercury. Do not use mercury containing fungicides on grains or animals.
Copper	High acid foods and beverages	Do not store high acid foods in copper utensils; use backflow prevention devices on beverage vending machines.
Lead	High acid food and beverages	Do not use vessels containing lead.
Preservatives and Food Additives: Sulfiting agents	Fresh fruits, Vegetables, Shrimp, Lobster, and Wine	Sulfiting agents added to a product in a processing plant must be declared on labeling. Do not use on raw produce in food establishments.
Flavor enhancers: Mono-sodium glutamate (MSG)	Asian or Latin American food	Avoid using excessive amounts
Chemicals used in retail establishments (*e.g., lubricants, cleaners, sanitizers, cleaning compounds, and paints*)	Any food could become contaminated	Address through SOPs for proper labeling, storage, handling, and use of chemicals; retain Material Safety Data

Figure 4

Another requirement limits chemicals on the premises to those required for the operation and maintenance of the food establishment. For example, chemicals such as paint thinner or gasoline are not allowed.

Preventative Measures

Chemical hazard-preventative measures include:

- Only buy from approved, reputable distributors
- Separate and secure storage, never above food
- Limited access, see intentional contamination below
- Staff training and monitoring
- Only have necessary products and use as directed
- Original containers with intact labels
- Discard if containers or lids are damaged

Allergen Hazards

Food allergens are naturally occurring chemical hazards. However, unlike the chemical hazards in the previous section, which are dangerous to everyone, food allergies and other types of food hypersensitivities only affect some people. Within the affected group, which includes millions of people, their antibodies elicit an abnormal immune response to certain foods. The most severe reactions involve anaphylactic shock, requiring an immediate epidural shot (epi-pen) or emergency medical attention to treat a potentially fatal allergic reaction. There is no cure for food allergies, so consumers must avoid them.

Annex 4, Page 11

Figure 5

> **KEY TERM** Allergen is a substance, often a protein, that causes an allergic response that can be severe or fatal to some. Examples include pollen, molds, and certain foods.

The Big 9 — Major Food Allergens

Annex 4, Page 529

There are more than 160 foods that are known to cause food allergies in sensitive individuals. The FDA has identified nine major food allergens based on scientific consensus, known as the Big 9. The Big 9 account for 90 percent of food allergies and severe allergic reactions among people in the U.S.

1-201.10

Peanuts	*Milk*	*Fish*
Tree Nuts	*Eggs*	*Crustacean Shellfish*
Wheat	*Soybeans*	*Sesame*

The following table is information on allergens from Annex 4, Table 2a (see Figure 6) of the FDA Food Code, titled **Naturally Occurring Chemical Hazards at Retail, Along with Their Associated Foods and Control Measures**.

Annex 4, Table 2a

Naturally Occurring Chemical Hazards	Associated Foods	Control Measures
Allergens	Foods containing or contacted by: Milk, Egg, Fish, Crustacean, Shellfish, Tree nuts, Wheat, Peanuts, Soybeans, or Sesame	Use a rigorous sanitation regime to prevent cross-contact between allergenic and non-allergenic ingredients.

Figure 6

Prevention and Cross-Contact

Food establishments must actively work to prevent allergic reactions through training, communication, and standard operating procedures (SOPs), including cross-contact avoidance during the food preparation process.

Annex 3, 2-103.11

Menus

The menu must list allergy information for any offerings containing, wholly or partially as an ingredient, any of the Big 9 foods. This includes optional sides, sauces, add-ons, desserts, or beverages on the menu.

3-603.12(C)

LUNCH MENU
—

Served daily from 12pm-5pm

Classic American Hamburger
Juicy quarterpound patty topped with bacon, tomatoes, pepperjack and the house steak sauce*

Crispy Chicken on Foccacia
Grilled chicken breast spread with a sesame pesto, grilled sweet peppers & zucchini*

*FOOD ALLERGY NOTICE

Please be advised that food prepared on the premises may contain the following ingredients: Milk, Eggs, Wheat, Sesame, Peanuts, Tree Nuts, Fish & Shellfish

Service

2-103.11(O)

When taking food orders, servers should inquire about allergies. Suppose someone identifies themselves as having a food allergy. In that case, the server can take precautions similar to the "employee story" at the beginning of this chapter, which includes pointing out potential hazards in items ordered by others at the table and informing the kitchen to use extra caution. To do this, service staff must be trained on the ingredients in each menu item. Finally, the allergen-free plates must be clearly identified when the food is served.

Figure 7

Preparation

Annex 3, Page 18

Avoiding cross-contact in the kitchen is the primary method of preventing allergic reactions from consumed food. Cross-contact describes the accidental introduction of an allergen into food that would not intentionally contain that allergen as an ingredient. Most cross-contact can be avoided through control of the environment during food storage, preparation, and service.

> **KEY TERM** Cross-contact occurs when allergens are transferred to a food which does not contain the allergen by the actions of a food employee.

Annex 3, 4-602.11

The FDA Food Code requires that food contact surfaces of equipment and utensils that have contacted any of the Big 9 ingredients, such as fish, must be cleaned and sanitized prior to contacting other types of foods. One strategy to avoid cross-contact is using special allergen equipment, such as cutting boards and utensils (see Figure 8), when working with foods intended for a sensitive consumer. This equipment must be cleaned and sanitized between uses but never used on allergenic foods.

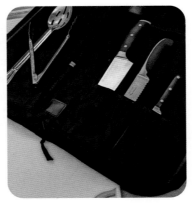

Figure 8

Cooking and freezing do not destroy the protein in food, which causes allergic reactions. Therefore, managing cross-contact is vital when cooking allergenic foods. Allergens can transfer (i.e., cross-contact) by direct contact between two foods in an oven or indirectly through grease in a deep fryer. For example, when preparing pork and fish, simultaneously, adequate spacing shall be maintained.

Symptoms of Food Allergies

Symptoms from an allergic reaction can happen within minutes and range from mild irritation to anaphylactic shock. Train your staff to identify food allergy symptoms and how to respond. Quick action can limit consumption and allow more time for potentially life-saving medical assistance. Some of these symptoms are not always related to an allergic reaction, so seeking proper care and diagnosis from a healthcare provider is crucial.

Annex 4, Page 11

KEY TERM Anaphylaxis is an allergic reaction to an allergen that can be severe or fatal to some.

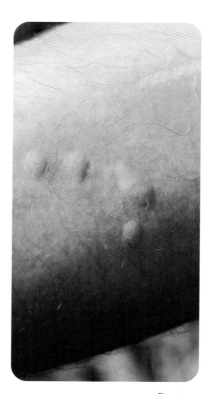

Symptoms of allergic reactions can include:

- Hives, rash, itchy skin
- Tingling or itchy sensation in the mouth
- Nausea, vomiting, diarrhea
- Abdominal cramps
- Coughing, wheezing
- Dizziness, lightheadedness
- Swelling of the throat and vocal cords
- Difficulty breathing
- Face, tongue, or lips swelling
- Loss of consciousness

Figure 9

Food Allergen Labeling

The FDA requires all ingredients containing a Big 9 allergen to be labeled, even if they are exempted from labeling by being a spice, flavoring, coloring, or incidental additive. An example of this labeling can be seen in the adjacent photo (Figure 10) which states "CONTAINS WHEAT INGREDIENTS".

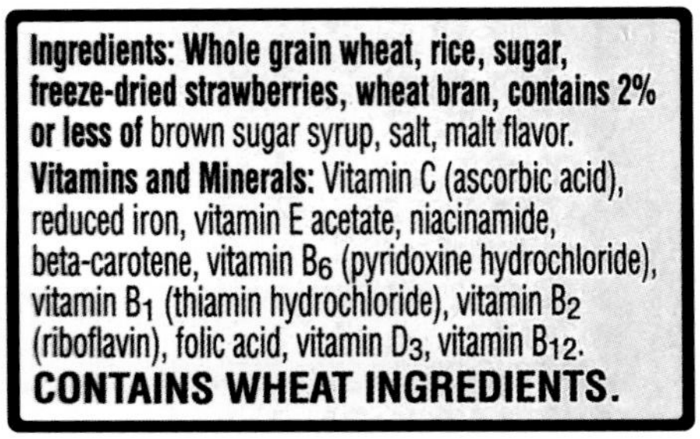

Ingredients: Whole grain wheat, rice, sugar, freeze-dried strawberries, wheat bran, **contains 2% or less of** brown sugar syrup, salt, malt flavor. **Vitamins and Minerals:** Vitamin C (ascorbic acid), reduced iron, vitamin E acetate, niacinamide, beta-carotene, vitamin B_6 (pyridoxine hydrochloride), vitamin B_1 (thiamin hydrochloride), vitamin B_2 (riboflavin), folic acid, vitamin D_3, vitamin B_{12}. **CONTAINS WHEAT INGREDIENTS.**

Figure 10

Gluten

Consumers susceptible to celiac disease require information about foods containing gluten, which must be strictly avoided. In certain grains, such as wheat, rye, and barley, gluten describes a group of proteins that causes an immune response that attacks and damages the small intestine lining. Most commercially available oat products also contain gluten due to cross-contact during processing.

Manager's Responsibility

According to the FDA Food Code, foodservice managers need to be aware of the severe nature of food allergies, including:

- Allergic reactions, anaphylaxis, and death
- Know the nine major food allergens (aka the Big 9)
- Understand food allergen ingredient identities and labeling
- Avoid cross-contact during food preparation and service

Food allergy awareness is a food safety training duty of the Person in Charge. For staff to safely perform their responsibilities related to food allergies, they must be adequately trained.

During an inspection, a person in charge (PIC) must demonstrate their knowledge of foods identified as major food allergens (i.e., the Big 9) and the symptoms that a major food allergen could cause in a sensitive individual experiencing an allergic reaction.

Cross-contamination

Preventing the transfer of pathogens from dirty hands, utensils, or equipment to clean equipment or ready-to-eat foods is essential. Failing to do so causes cross-contamination. For example, the same knife used to cut raw meat is then used to cut up salad ingredients without being washed and sanitized between tasks. Cross-contamination is a significant source of foodborne illnesses affecting the health of thousands of consumers each year.

Dirty		**Clean**
Hands		RTE Foods
Utensils		Utensils
Equipment		Equipment
Food contact surfaces		Food contact surfaces

Unless being combined as ingredients to be mixed/cooked as a single recipe, the adjacent photo (Figure 11) depicts an example of unacceptable cross-contamination, where raw meat and ready-to-eat foods are on the same cutting board, using the same knife. Both the utensil and equipment are considered contaminated by the presence of the raw chicken.

3-302.11

The corrective action would be to discard the RTE foods and use a separate (clean and sanitized) cutting board and knife to prepare the onions. An acceptable exception would be if the onions were cooked with the raw chicken in a stew. This introduces a pathogen kill-step for both the chicken and the onions.

Figure 11

KEY TERM Cross-contamination **occurs when a pathogen, chemical, or physical substance has been transferred to a** food **or beverage. The result can be potentially harmful, causing foodborne illness if consumed.**

Associated Bad Bugs

Bacteria is a common contaminant, and since the cross-contamination is unknown, the conditions are often ideal for bacteria to quickly grow to unsafe levels and cause foodborne illness. The contamination of food by **viruses** results from cross-contamination by ill food employees or unclean equipment and utensils. **Parasitic** infections are commonly associated with cross-contamination of ready-to-eat food with raw an-

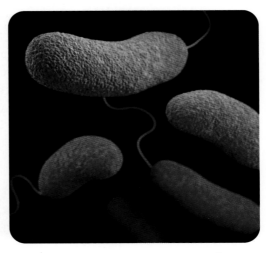

Figure 12

imal foods, untreated water, or contaminated equipment or utensils. Viruses and parasites do not grow in food, so control is focused on preventing their introduction (i.e. cross-contamination). Hazards associated with cross-contamination:

Hazard	Associated Food	Control Measures
Campylobacter jejuni	Poultry, raw milk	Cooking, handwashing, **prevention of cross-contamination**
Shiga toxin-producing E. coli	Raw ground beef, raw seed sprouts, raw milk, unpasteurized juice, foods contaminated by infected food workers via fecal-oral route	Cooking, no bare hand contact with RTE foods, employee health policy, handwashing, **prevention of cross-contamination**, pasteurization or treatment of juice
Listeria monocytogenes	Raw meat and poultry, fresh soft cheese, paté, smoked seafood, deli meats, deli salads	Cooking, date marking, cold holding, handwashing, **prevention of cross-contamination**
Vibrio spp.	Seafood, shellfish	Cooking, approved source, **prevention of cross-contamination**, cold holding

Figure 13

Manager's Responsibility

Active managerial control over personal hygiene and cross-contamination requires the implementation of specific control measures in all aspects of the operation. It is crucial to implement all of these control measures in a food operation:

2-103.11

- **No bare hand contact with ready-to-eat foods**
  To prevent the transfer of viruses, bacteria, or parasites from hands to food

Annex 4, Page 30

- **Proper handwashing**
  To prevent the transfer of viruses, bacteria, or parasites from hands to food

- **Restriction or exclusion of ill employees**
  To prevent the transfer of viruses, bacteria, or parasites from hands to food

- **Prevention of cross-contamination**
  Between ready-to-eat food, clean and sanitized food-contact surfaces with soiled cutting boards, utensils, aprons, etc., or raw animal foods.

From the FDA Food Code:

2-103.11(N)

Employees are preventing cross-contamination of ready-to-eat food with bare hands by properly using suitable utensils such as deli tissue, spatulas, tongs, single-use gloves, or dispensing equipment.

Preventative Measures

Specific cross-contamination prevention measures in the flow of food:

- **Delivery**
  - Examine delivery truck and products for signs of potential cross-contamination

Annex 5, Page 16

- **Storage**
  - Store RTE Foods above meat, poultry, seafood, and raw shell eggs
  - Separate raw animal foods by type, such as beef, fish, lamb, pork, and poultry

- **Preparation**
  - Use single-use gloves or utensils when working with RTE Foods or handling ice when used as an ingredient
  - Use separate cutting boards, surfaces, and plates for raw meats, poultry, and seafood
  - Keep RTE Foods separate from non-RTE Foods

- **Service**
  - Only touch plates and utensils by their edges and handles

Color-coded Cutting Boards

Annex 5, Page 17

Annex 5, Page 31

It is essential to separate foods in a ready-to-eat form from raw animal foods during storage, preparation, holding, and display to prevent them from becoming contaminated by pathogens that may be present in or on the raw animal foods. One method of accomplishing food separation is by using color-coded cutting boards. The color-coded cutting board uses:

Green Produce	**Red** Raw Meats	**Blue** Seafood
Yellow Raw Poultry	**White** Dairy/Pastry	**Beige** Cooked Meats

Washed vegetables are prepared on green NSF-certified commercial cutting boards to prevent cross-contamination. Good training results in raw meats never being cut on a green cutting board. This color coding is also a visual aid for managers. Suppose someone is observed cutting raw meat on a green cutting board. In that case, the manager can quickly step in and take corrective action, which includes discarding contaminated food, sanitizing surfaces, equipment, utensils, and retraining.

Figure 14

Annex 3, Page 177

When to Clean and Sanitize

Clean and sanitize all equipment, utensils, and surfaces that touch food:

- After each use
- When changing product
- Between meat species
- Frequently when preparing large amounts
- Between raw and cooked meats or RTE Foods

Figure 15

Intentional Contamination

Another food hazard to consider is the intentional contamination of food, which the FDA describes as adulterated food. To be clear, in this section, the result of food becoming contaminated means a person is deliberately trying to cause harm to others. The motivations for this vary and may be carried out, for example, by:

Annex 3, Page 72

- Disgruntled employees or competitors
- Family or relationship associations
- Domestic or foreign terrorists
- A person suffering from mental illness

> **KEY TERM** Adulterated **describes** food **that bears or contains any poisonous substance which may render it injurious to health.**

Food fraud is another form of adulteration, not necessarily resulting in harmful contamination; the FDA describes this as economically motivated adulteration. Motivated by increased profits, a food processor or operation will leave out or substitute valuable ingredients and engage in false labeling (e.g., on a product or printed menu). For example, olive oil may be combined with less expensive vegetable oil but labeled and sold as 100% pure olive oil.

Annex 3, Page 73

When it comes to prevention, the FDA distinguishes between accidental and international contamination as follows:

- Food **Safety** is protection from accidental contamination of food
- Food **defense** is protection from intentional contamination of food

Preventative Measures

Annex 2, Page 78
Annex 3, Page 17

The FDA recommends and provides many resources for creating a **food defense program**. The program is designed to identify vulnerabilities and mitigation strategies. Although not actively promoted by the FDA today, the mnemonic device ALERT is still used to train staff and help them remember five essential points regarding food safety as it relates to intentional contamination.

ALERT

Assure

- Know your supplier
- Supervise offloading of incoming materials
- Request locked and/or sealed vehicles/containers/railcars

Look

- Implement a system for handling products
- Track materials
- Store product labels in a secure location and destroy outdated or discarded product labels
- Limit access and inspect facilities
- Keep track of finished products
- Encourage your warehousing operations to practice food defense measures

Employees

- Conduct background checks on staff
- Know who belongs in your facility
- Establish an identification system for employees
- Limit access by staff
- Prevent customer's access to critical areas of your facility

Reports

- Periodically evaluate the effectiveness of your security management system
- Perform random food defense inspections
- Establishment and maintenance of records
- Evaluate lessons learned

Threats

- Hold any product that you believe may have been affected
- Contact the Food and Drug Administration or USDA/Food Safety and Inspection Service

Manager's Responsibility

The FDA created a program that managers can use to inform and remind food employees that they are the FIRST line of defense at preventing intentional food contamination.

F Follow the company food defense plan and procedures

I Inspect your work area and surrounding areas

R Recognize anything out of the ordinary

S Secure all ingredients, supplies, and finished products

T Tell management if you notice anything unusual or suspicious

Managers can also have staff take the FDA's Food Defense 101 training found online at: https://www.fda.gov/food/food-defense-training-education/food-defense-101-front-line-employee

Summary

The theme of this chapter is to identify hazards and understand the necessary tools to prevent them from contaminating food. Managers must train and monitor staff on the steps necessary to avoid cross-contact, cross-contamination, and intentional contamination.

Preventing cross-contamination includes proper handwashing, protective coverings, good personal hygiene, separating raw ingredients from RTE foods, cleaning and sanitizing equipment, and using color-coded cutting boards. Avoiding cross-contact involves understanding that the Big 9 ingredients cannot come into contact with other foods to prevent serious allergic reactions. Finally, staff are the FIRST line of defense when it comes to preventing intentional contamination of food, with the goal of causing harm to others.

- Food contaminants include biological, physical, chemical, and allergens

- Cross-contamination happens when pathogens have been transferred to food

- Cross-contact happens when allergens are transferred to another food normally safe from allergens, creating a potential for an allergic reaction when consumed

- Intentional contamination, or adulterated food, happens when an individual deliberately contaminates food with the intention of harming others

- A food defense program is intended to combat intentional contamination

- A food safety program is intended to prevent accidental food contamination

The Student's Workbook

As assigned by your instructor, use the separate Student's Workbook to work independently or in groups. Activities for this week's chapter include:

- Create a "Big 9" poster

- Vote on the best (and completely accurate) poster in the class

- Watch the video and reflect

- Discuss the risks of each ingredient in the chicken stock recipe

- Make a list of equipment needed

- Produce the recipe

- Review the cleaning and sanitizing checklist

- Fill out the recipe and cost form

- End of chapter review video

Review Questions

Use these questions to check your knowledge of the material in this chapter. *Your instructor has the answers.*

1 Which of the following is not a chemical hazard?

a. Cleaners

b. Glass

c. Pesticides

d. Medications

2 Unintentionally consuming a bone could cause the following symptom.

a. Choking

b. Diarrhea

c. Hives

d. Yellowing of the skin

3 Which building piping material is a potential food hazard?

a. Carpet

b. Pewter

c. Copper

d. Zinc

4 Relative to food, chemicals can never be stored _____.

a. across from food

b. in a separate locked room

c. above food

d. below food

5 Which is not one of the Big 9 allergen foods?

a. Pork

b. Eggs

c. Soybeans

d. Sesame

6 Transferring pathogens to food is called _____.

a. cross-contact

b. inexperienced

c. mixed food corruption

d. cross-contamination

7 Transferring an allergen to a non-allergen food is called _____.

a. cross-contact

b. inexperienced

c. mixed food corruption

d. cross-contamination

8 A program intended to prevent intentional contamination.

a. Food defense

b. Food safety

c. FDA Food Code

d. HCAPP

Chapter 05

TCS Foods and Controls

Introduction

The theme of this chapter is to understand the necessary controls to prevent foodborne illness, especially with Time/Temperature Control for Safety Foods (TCS Foods). Food managers must train to identify TCS Foods and properly monitor time and temperature.

This chapter covers the primary types of food hazards and the various controls used to prevent them from contaminating food. This involves understanding TCS foods, cross-contamination, intentional contamination, and the controls used to avoid foodborne illness. Controls are managerial methods used to implement, train, enforce, correct, retrain, and monitor food to ensure its safety within the flow of food. For example, thermometers are used to check a food's internal temperature, time is tracked to limit bacterial growth, and logs are kept to validate the process. All this and more are covered in this chapter.

Key Terms

Keep an eye out for these essential topics:

- Flow of Food
- Temperature danger zone
- Bimetallic Stemmed Thermometer
- Infrared Thermometer
- TCS foods
- Temperature measuring device
- Thermometer calibration
- Logs

Objectives

After working through this chapter, you should be able to explain the following to friends and family:

- Describe the flow of food
- Explain what TCS Foods are
- Describe the temperature danger zone
- Understand the types of thermometers and their uses
- Know how to calibrate a bimetallic thermometer
- Explain how to monitor time and temperature

Devin,
Line Cook

Devin was tired. He was tired of working so many hours and the bad habits at the California-style diner. They were open 24 hours a day and served a great breakfast all day long. He worked behind the counter in the kitchen area, which was an open galley kitchen, fully visible to the customers.

Yesterday was the final straw, and he was looking for a new job. The health inspector came in to do a site visit, and things didn't go well. Beyond the fact that most staff didn't clean their hands properly, the place was generally a mess. They had a delicious chili that was added to the menu in the evening, but the health inspector ordered them to throw it all away as it was still in the temperature danger zone (TDZ) from the night before. That was just the start.

Other complaints were they had food items stored on the floor in the dry storage, and not a minimum of 6 inches off the floor. The countertop cooler, used for salad and sandwich items, was running hot. It was at 45°F (7°C) and did not recover while the inspection occurred. More embarrassment came when they looked at the two reach-in freezers. The manager tried to play off that one must have just gone down. The inspector pointed out the mold growing on the gaskets due to warm, humid, and dirty conditions made that unlikely. When the manager started to argue with the inspector, Devin knew this was not somewhere he could stay.

The following day Devin was hired at an up-market southwestern grill. He felt great during the interview as they not only offered him the job but promised they would pay for him to work on the food safety manager certification. He was excited to work somewhere he could finally be proud of, with spotlessly clean and correctly functioning equipment in a professionally run kitchen.

Food Safety Controls

With the many hazards in mind, we will now focus on the control measures a food manager can employ to monitor food, keep it safe, and prevent foodborne illness. Food safety controls start with understanding the flow of food, what TCS foods are, and then carefully monitoring time and temperature as food travels from receiving to service.

Before getting into the details, let's first take a brief look at what is legally required of food operation (in municipalities that have adopted the FDA Food Code). When studying for a test in school, it is essential to review the grading rubric to know what you will be graded on. Similarly, knowing what the food inspector will be looking for when they arrive for a surprise inspection in a food operation is helpful. Consider the following FDA Food Code instructions to the inspector regarding time and temperature:

Figure 1

From the FDA Food Code:

Annex 5, Page 14

Early in the inspection, temperatures of time/temperature control for safety foods (TCS) should be taken. For example, if inspecting in the morning, inspectors should check the temperatures of last night's stored leftovers. If inspecting in the afternoon, inspectors should check the temperatures of foods prepared that morning that are now cooling. Also, inspectors should ask whether any foods are currently being cooked or reheated.

While reflecting on this inspection requirement, let's set the stage for the remainder of this chapter. Consider the following table and note the importance of time and/or temperature in preventing foodborne illnesses.

Food	Hazard	Control Measure	Method
Baked meatloaf or chicken	*Salmonella spp.*	Refrigeration at 41°F (5°C) or below	Temperature
Baked meatloaf or chicken	*Clostridium perfringens or Bacillus cereus*	Hot Holding at 135°F (57°C) or above OR Time Control	Time OR Temperature
Baked meatloaf	*E. coli*	Cooking at 155°F (68°C) for 17 seconds	Time AND Temperature
Baked chicken	*Campylobacter*	Cooking at 165°F (74°C) or above	Temperature

Figure 2

The Flow of Food

The **flow of food** in a food operation is the path that food travels from receiving through service to the consumer. Several activities or stages comprise the flow of food and are called **operational steps**.

Annex 4, Page 26

Most foods produced in a food operation can be categorized into one of three preparation processes, depicted in the adjacent diagram, based on the number of times the food passes through the temperature danger zone between 41°F and 135°F (5°C–57°C).

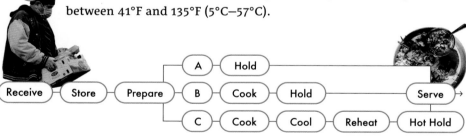

Figure 3

Description of the three preparation processes:

- **Process A: Food Preparation with No Cook Step**
  There is no cook step to destroy pathogens. This category includes raw, ready-to-eat food like sashimi, raw oysters, and salads. Components of these foods are received raw and not cooked before consumption.

- **Process B: Preparation for Same-Day Service**
  There is only one trip through the temperature danger zone. Food is usually cooked and held hot until served, e.g., fried chicken, but can also be cooked and served immediately.

- **Process C: Complex Food Preparation**
  There are always two or more complete trips through the temperature danger zone. This complex food preparation process usually involves foods prepared in large volumes or in advance for next-day service.

The adjacent diagram depicts the number of times food goes through the temperature danger zone in each of the three preparation categories (A, B, and C) listed above. Additionally, the following list corresponds to the numbers (1, 2, and 3) in the diagram:

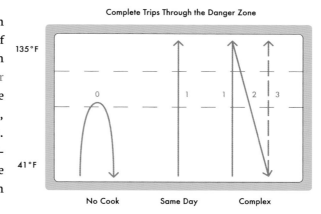

Figure 4

- **Zero Passes**
  There is no cook step involved in this flow; although foods may still enter the danger zone, they do not pass all the way through it.

- **One Pass**
  Foods are cooked and then served directly; this is called same-day service.

- **Three Passes**
  Foods are cooked (first pass), cooled (second pass), and then reheated (third pass).

Time/Temperature Control for Safety

Some foods can become hazardous if they spend too much time in the temperature danger zone-where bacteria that may be present in or on the food can quickly grow to unsafe levels and cause foodborne illness when consumed. These foods are called **TCS Foods** because time and/or temperature must be monitored and controlled to keep the food safe for consumption.

KEY TERM Time/Temperature Control for Safety Food (TCS Food) is a food that requires time and/or temperature control for safety (TCS) to limit pathogenic growth or toxin formation.

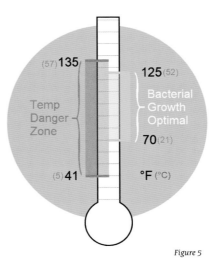

Figure 5

The **temperature danger zone** occurs when food is between 41°F–135°F (5°C–57°C). Within this range, bacterial growth potential is highest between 70°F–125°F (21°C–52°C).

Time/Temperature   **Control**   **Safety**

Figure 6

Time/Temperature

Time and Temperature are monitored

Control

Proactive and reactive measures are taken to control time and temperature abuse

Safety

The goal is to prevent bacterial growth and keep food safe

Which Foods are TCS Foods?

Some foods are defined as TCS Foods based on intrinsic properties such as pH and a_w levels, while others become TCS foods when they are cut in the food preparation process. Additionally, some TCS Foods become non-TCS foods when heat treated or packaged in a certain way.

The foods that become TCS Foods after being cut include produce such as melons, leafy greens, and tomatoes. These items therefore require time and/or temperature control for safety and should be refrigerated at 41°F or lower to prevent any pathogens that may be present from multiplying.

Figures 7-9

Foods prepared at the food operation may also become TCS Foods when they contain TCS Food ingredients. For example, a pie with meringue topping, meat salads, or fettuccine alfredo with chicken.

Annex 3, Page 5

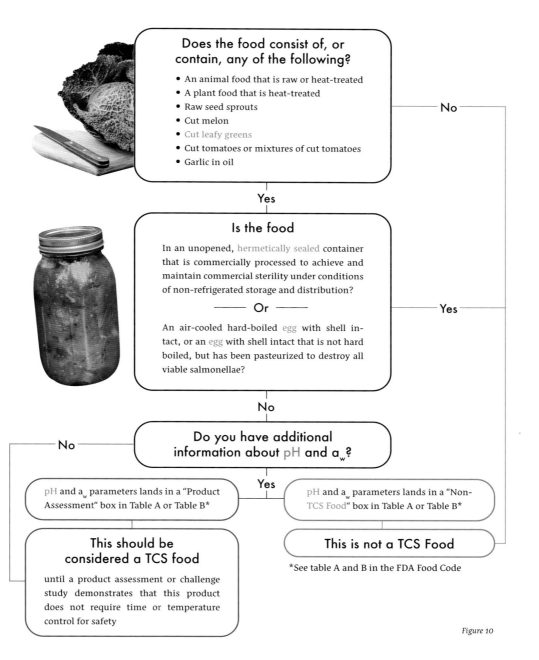

Does the food consist of, or contain, any of the following?

- An animal food that is raw or heat-treated
- A plant food that is heat-treated
- Raw seed sprouts
- Cut melon
- Cut leafy greens
- Cut tomatoes or mixtures of cut tomatoes
- Garlic in oil

No

Yes

Is the food

In an unopened, hermetically sealed container that is commercially processed to achieve and maintain commercial sterility under conditions of non-refrigerated storage and distribution?

——— Or ———

An air-cooled hard-boiled egg with shell intact, or an egg with shell intact that is not hard boiled, but has been pasteurized to destroy all viable salmonellae?

Yes

No

Do you have additional information about pH and a_w?

No

Yes

pH and a_w parameters lands in a "Product Assessment" box in Table A or Table B*

pH and a_w parameters lands in a "Non-TCS Food" box in Table A or Table B*

This should be considered a TCS food

until a product assessment or challenge study demonstrates that this product does not require time or temperature control for safety

This is not a TCS Food

*See table A and B in the FDA Food Code

Figure 10

The following are examples of non-TCS Foods:

- An air-cooled hard-boiled egg with its shell intact

- Pasteurized egg with its shell intact (not hard-boiled)

- Food in an unopened hermetically sealed container

- Food designated as a non-TCS Food based on its pH or A_w values

Monitoring Temperature

The FDA Food Code requires food establishments to monitor cooking temperatures routinely. The appropriate temperature measuring device must be accessible to food employees.

Monitoring a food's temperature throughout the flow of food is essential to keep food safe by killing dangerous pathogens or preventing them from growing to unsafe levels and causing foodborne illness when consumed. This section will review the thermometers used to measure a food's temperature, how to calibrate a thermometer, and how and when to take measurements.

Figure 11

It is crucial to keep in mind that all thermometers should be cleaned and sanitized between uses to prevent cross-contamination. Sanitation is accomplished by using alcohol swabs or washing with soap and water.

KEY TERM Temperature measuring device means a thermometer, thermocouple, thermistor, or other device that indicates the temperature of food, air, or water.

Types of Thermometers

The correct **temperature measuring device** and technique are required to get an accurate temperature measurement of TCS foods. Food inspectors will check for the presence of required thermometers and their proper use.

Figure 12

Thermometer Type	Indicator	Measures	What
Bimetallic Stemmed	Dial	Internal temperature	Thick foods
Thermocouple and Thermistor	Digital	Internal temperature, air	Thick or thin foods, coolers
Infrared	Digital	Surface temperature	Surface of food
Candy/ Deep Fryer	Analog	Submerged while cooking	candy fudge/ fried chicken

Figure 13

Bimetallic Stemmed Thermometer

Highlights: Larger diameter probe, thicker foods, no power required
Temperature-sensing area: from dimple to tip (must be fully submerged)
Temperature range: 0°F-220°F (-18°C-104°C)

Given its size and portability, the bimetallic stemmed thermometer is a popular thermometer in the kitchen. Most chef aprons and jackets have a place to store this type of thermometer.

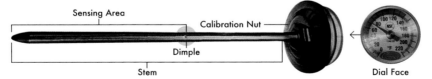

A properly calibrated bimetallic stemmed thermometer can accurately measure the temperatures of thicker foods, such as roasts, casseroles, and soups. The entire **sensing area**, i.e., from the dimple to the tip of the probe, must be inserted into the food, touching the food's geometric center, for an accurate measurement. The sensing area is approximately 2"–2.5" (51 mm—64

Annex 3, Page 168

Bimetallic Stemmed Thermometer Cont.

mm) long. The temperature measurement displayed by the dial is the average of the food-contact area along this length.

Due to the (larger) diameter of the probe and the length of the sensing area this thermometer is not well suited to measure the internal temperature of thin foods such as hamburger patties, boneless chicken breasts, and fish filets. However, when necessary, the probe should be inserted sideways, and extended to the center of the food. An accurate measurement cannot be achieved by inserting just the tip into the food using a bimetallic stemmed thermometer.

Thermocouple/Thermistor Thermometer

Highlights: Smaller diameter probe, thick or thin foods, power (batteries)
Temperature-sensing area: at the tip of the probe
Temperature range: Thermocouple:-40°F-1000°F (-40°C-538°C)
                Thermistor:-40°F-300°F (-40°C-149°C)

Thermocouples and thermistors are similar and mainly vary by the internal method used to derive the digitally displayed temperature. The sensing area is consolidated to the tip of the probe. Therefore, there is no need for a dimple on the stem. This thermometer type is ideal for thin foods, given its smaller diameter and consolidated sensing area.

 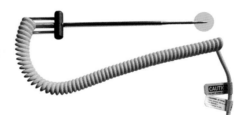

Many thermocouples and thermistors are modular systems that include base unit and multiple detachable probe options. The FDA Food Code requires a food handler to use the appropriate probes for the food being tested. This modular device has specialized probes to measure liquids, surfaces, and air. Thermocouple and Thermistor probe types:

- Air probe   *For measuring ambient air temperatures*
- Penetration probe   *For measurements in semi-solid foods*
- Immersion probe   *For measurements in liquids, sauces, and gravies*
- Surface probe   *For measuring surface temperatures*

KEY TERM Thermocouples are comprised of two types of metals connected at one end. When that end is heated or cooled, the voltage created can be correlated to the temperature.

KEY TERM Thermistors, aka thermally sensitive resistors, are composed of materials with known resistance. The temperature is derived from the known resistance of the material.

Infrared Thermometer

Highlights: measures surface temperature, power (batteries) required
Temperature-sensing area: non-contact laser
Temperature range: -58°F-716°F (-50°C-380°C)

The surface temperature of food (and equipment) can be measured using an infrared thermometer. An accurate reading requires the device to be held close to the surface but not touching. Additionally, any wrappers or packaging must be removed to expose the food's surface, creating a direct line of sight for the sensor.

From the FDA Food Code:

Annex 5, Page 20

Using an infrared thermometer for verifying holding temperatures is not consistent with Food Code requirements since verifying only the surface temperature of the food may not alert food handlers or inspectors to problems that exist under the food's surface.

Other Thermometers

Candy/Fryer thermometers are used to keep track of the current cooking temperature by submerging it into the product or frying oil. This helps avoid under or overcooking. The high-temperature design, up to 400°F (204°C), allows the thermometer to remain in the product while cooking. Care should be taken when adding or removing the device.

Other Thermometers Cont.

A **Hot Holding thermometer** is placed in an oven and used to ensure the air temperature is correct when holding cooked foods for service. Notice this example includes FDA Food Code safety guidelines on the face, as a helpful reminder to food handlers.

Thermometer Calibration

4-502.11
Annex 7, Page 45

Bimetallic stemmed thermometers are sensitive instruments that require regular calibration to ensure accurate readings. Dropping them or switching from measuring foods at extreme temperature differences can result in inaccurate readings. Accuracy is essential, especially when considering the lower range of the temperature danger zone and the highest range of required refrigeration are the same numbers: 41°F (5°C). Therefore, being off a little can make a difference and lead to food contamination.

When to calibrate (followed by sanitization):

- Before each shift
- In preparation for deliveries
- When dropped or jarred
- When exposed to extreme temperature differences

There are two methods for calibrating bimetallic thermometers: ice-point and boiling-point. If ice is available, the ice-point is preferred since the food operation's altitude does not need to be taken into consideration as discussed next.

- **Method 1: Ice and water**
  1. Fill a container with ice cubes (use crushed ice if available), then add cold potable water and let it sit for 4 to 5 minutes to form a watery slurry. FYI: do not add salt, as this makes the reading inaccurate.

  2. Insert the thermometer stem's sensing area into the container, making sure not to touch the side, and let it sit until the dial stops moving.

  3. The temperature reading should be 32°F (0°C) after 30 seconds. Recalibrate the thermometer as required by adjusting the calibration nut using a wrench. Log discrepancies and recalibration to maintain records should an inspector require them.

Figure 14

● **Method 2: Boiling Water**

1. Bring a clean container of potable water to a boil.

2. Once the water is boiling, insert the thermometer stem's sensing area into the container, making sure not to touch the side or bottom, and let it sit until the dial stops moving.

3. The temperature reading should be 212°F (100°C). Log discrepancies and recalibration to maintain records should an inspector require them.

Figure 15

At higher altitudes, water boils at lower temperatures. For every 550 feet (168m) above sea level, subtract 1°F (~0.5°C).

When to Measure Food Temperature

In addition to knowing how to calibrate a thermometer and measure a food's internal temperature, a food employee must also know when to take a measurement. Below are examples from across the flow of food within a food operation. Also, note that thermometers must be properly washed, rinsed, and sanitized before using them to prevent cross-contamination.

2-103.11(H)

Examples of when to use a thermometer within the flow of food:

● **Receiving:**

Measure the temperature of RTE Foods with a sanitized and calibrated thermometer.

1. Cold foods must be less than 41°F (5°C).
2. Hot deliveries need to be greater than 135°F (57°C). Reject RTE Foods delivered at the wrong temperature.

3-202

● **Storage:**

Check the air temperature multiple times a day in the walk-in cooler and freezer with a probe thermometer and record the readings.

1. Walk-in cooler ambient air temperature: 35°F–38°F (2°C-3°C)
2. Walk-in cooler internal food temperature: 41°F (5°C) or below
3. Walk-in freezer: 0°F (-18°C) or below, which is well below freezing

3-402

● **Cooking:**

Use a clean and calibrated thermometer to check the final cooking temperature.

3-401

● **Cooling:**

Use a clean and calibrated thermometer to check the temperature at the center of the food. Make sure that it reaches:

3-501.15

1. Cool to 70°F (21°C) within 2 hours
2. Cool to 41°F (5°C) within an additional 4 hours.

● **Reheat:**

Use a sanitized and calibrated thermometer to make sure that 165° F is reached throughout the food each time food is reheated.

3-403

1. Reheat rapidly to 165°F (74°C) within 2 hours without interruption.

● **Hot holding:**

Keep food above 135 ° F (57°C), check with a sanitized and calibrated thermometer at determined frequency.

3-501.16(A)(1)

- **Cold holding:**
  Spot check cold holding procedures and temperatures with a sanitized and calibrated thermometer.
  1. 41°F (5°C) or below

- **Cleaning:**
  Prior to use, check the water temperature in the 3-compartment sink as follows:
  1. **Left sink:** 110°F (43°C) minimum.
  2. **Center sink:** No specific temperature required, but generally still hot.
  3. **Right sink:** Sanitizer manufacturer's recommended temperature. Generally warm to cold water. Alternatively, heat can be used in place of a sanitizer chemical. This involves a heating element in the right sink used to maintain 171°F (77°C) temperature, where the item to be cleaned is exposed for a minimum of 30 seconds.

Temperature readings should be recorded in a log. These logs can then be shown to the inspector as evidence of proper food management practices. The log can also be provided to authorities (e.g., CDC) in the event of a foodborne illness outbreak. Be sure to consider the temperature fields in the example logs in the next section, Monitoring Time.

Monitoring Time

This entire section on food safety controls has repeatedly mentioned time as a control. TCS foods can be time and/or temperature abused. The only way to carefully monitor time is to track it in **logs**. Similar to how some people use pill boxes to remember to take their medication, food safety logs help food employees to remember to record time and temperatures.

In a busy organization, it is easy to forget to take a reading, not remember if you took a reading, or assume one of the many other food co-workers took a reading. This is why logs are so important; a measurement never happened if an entry does not exist on a log. These logs can then be shown to the inspector as evidence of proper food management practices (e.g., an HACCP Plan—covered in chapter 13). The log can also be provided to authorities (e.g., CDC) in the event of a foodborne illness outbreak. Records should be kept for at least 6 months.

Several example logs are provided below, with sample input to demonstrate important information typically recorded in a food operation. These logs generally are on a full sheet of paper attached to a clipboard. Blank originals are kept in the office and used to make additional copies when needed.

Reheating Temperature Log

The Food Code requires that foods are reheated to 165°F (75°C) within 2 hours.

Reheating Temperature Log

Date	Initials	Food Product	Reheat Time/Temperature				Corrective Action
			Start Time	Start Temp	End Time	End Temp	
1-1-23	DJS	Lasagna	8 am	41°F (5°C)	10 am	165°F (74°C)	
1-1-23	DJS	Baked Ziti	8 am	41°F (5°C)	10 am	*135°F (57°C)	Discarded

Figure 16

Cooling Temperature Log

The Food Code requires that foods not cooked for immediate service be cooled quickly to minimize time in the temperature danger zone and limit bacterial growth. The specific time and temperature requirements are as follows:

- Cool to 70°F (21°C) within 2 hours
- Cool to 41°F (5°C) within an additional 4 hours.

Note that commercial refrigeration equipment is designed to hold cold food temperatures, not cool large masses of food. Rapid chilling equipment is designed to quickly cool the food to acceptable temperatures by using very low temperatures and high air circulation rates.

Cooling Temperature Log

Date	Initials	Food Product	Cooling Time/Temperature						Corrective Action
			Final Temp	Time	2 Hrs	Time	4 Hrs	Time	
1-1-23	DJS	Lasagna	155°F (68°C)	8 am	70°F (21°C)	10 am	41°F (5°C)	12 am	
1-1-23	DJS	Baked Ziti	155°F (68°C)	8 am	*90°F (32°C)				Discarded

Figure 17

Refrigeration Temperature Log

Daily refrigeration temperature monitoring ensures food is stored at the proper temperature. When stored refrigerated food has been above 41°F (5°C) for more than 4 hours it must be discarded. Discarding an entire walk-in cooler full of food would be a significant financial loss for a food operation.

Annex 3, Page 160

From the FDA Food Code:

A temperature measuring device used to measure the air temperature in a refrigeration unit is not required to be as accurate as a food thermometer because the unit's temperature fluctuates with repeated opening and closing of the door and because accuracy in measuring internal food temperatures is of more significance.

Refrigeration Temperature Log

Date	Initials	Morning Temp	Noon Temp	Evening Temp	Corrective Action
1-1-23	DJS	41°F (5°C)	41°F (5°C)	41°F (5°C)	
1-1-23	DJS	41°F (5°C)	*41°F (5°C)		Checked several food temps

Figure 18

Food Temperature Log

The Food Code requires that cold foods be held at 41°F (5°C) and hot foods at 135°F (57°C). Temperatures must be checked and recorded every two hours.

Food Temperature Log

Date	Initials	Food Item	Time	Temperature	Corrective Action
1-1-23	DJS	Lasagna	8 am	135°F (57°C)	
1-1-23	DJS	Lasagna	10 am	135°F (57°C)	
1-1-23	DJS	Lasagna	12 am	*125°F (52°C)	Discarded

Figure 19

Manager's Responsibility

Annex 3 of the FDA Food Code states that an important duty of the manager, or Person in Charge, is to make sure that any required temperatures are achieved or maintained when foods are cooked, cooled, or held in a food establishment. By making it a duty of the Person in Charge to ensure that employees are monitoring food temperatures to verify the critical temperature limits, the likelihood of temperature abuse is reduced.

2-103.11

This includes oversight of temperature monitoring to ensure:

- That animal foods are being cooked to the required minimum temperatures to prevent the survival of pathogens that may be present.

- That cooked foods are being cooled rapidly to ensure that the growth of bacterial pathogens and toxin production is prevented.

- That foods that require temperature control for safety are being held at temperatures that adequately prevent pathogen growth and toxin production.

Summary

This chapter focused on the necessary controls to prevent foodborne illness, especially with Time/Temperature Control for Safety Foods (TCS Foods).

When working with TCS Foods it is imperative they are not time and/or temperature abused. Food employees must understand the temperature danger zone relative to the flow of food. For example, cooked food intended to be stored for later use must be cooled quickly from its final temperature, so the food spends minimal time in the temperature danger zone. The same is true when reheating the food for service. Finally, the necessary time/temperature measurements must be logged to ensure proper safety controls are being followed.

- The FDA Food Code describes three primary preparation processes within the flow of food: No cook, same-day service, and complex preparation.

- TCS stands for: Time/Temperature/Control for Safety.

- Foods that are susceptible to bacteria growth when in the temperature danger zone are considered TCS Foods.

- Color-coded cutting boards help keep raw ingredients separate from TCS foods.

- There are three primary types of thermometers: bimetallic, thermocouple/thermistor, and infrared.

- Bimetallic thermometers should be calibrated often using one of two methods: ice-point or boiling-point.

- Active managerial control means the manager, or person-in-charge (PIC), has implemented controls such as training and monitoring such that the food operation is fully compliant with the requirements of the Food Code.

The Student's Workbook

As assigned by your instructor, use the separate Student's Workbook to work independently or in groups. Activities for this week's chapter include:

- Explore effective cooling methods
- Watch the video and reflect
- Discuss the risks of each ingredient in the seafood gumbo recipe
- Make a list of equipment needed
- Produce the recipe
- Review the cleaning and sanitizing checklist
- Fill out the recipe and cost form
- End of chapter review video

Use these questions to check your knowledge of the material in this chapter. *Your instructor has the answers.*

1 Early in a visit, an inspector will check the temperature of _____.

a. cooked steaks

b. TCS Foods

c. stored vegetables

d. the freezer

2 Baked meatloaf should be stored at or below 41°F (5°C) to help prevent ____.

a. Salmonella spp.

b. Clostridium perfringens

c. E. coli

d. Campylobacter

3 Which is not a preparation process in the flow of food?

a. No cook step

b. Same-day service

c. Simple food step

d. Complex food preparation

4 The complex food preparation process takes food through the danger zone

a. once

b. twice

c. three times

d. none

5 The temperature danger zone is _____.

a. 41°F–135°F (5°C–57°C)

b. 70°F –125°F (21°C–52°C)

c. 32°F –125°F (0°C –52°C)

d. 70°F – 135°F (21°C– 57°C)

6 A thermometer with a dimple is called a _____.

a. Thermocouple

b. Infrared

c. Candy

d. Bimetallic Stemmed

7 Food must be reheated to 165°F (74°C) within _____.

a. 1 hour

b. 30 minutes

c. 2 hours

d. 24 hours

8 Food must be cooled to 70°F (21°C) for storage within _____.

a. 2 hours

b. 3 hours

c. 4 hours

d. 6 hours

Chapter 06

Sources & Receiving

Introduction

A manager has a lot of choices when it comes to the source of foods purchased for use in a food operation. Associated with those choices is a responsibility to follow the law and protect the consumer from contamination and food fraud. The U.S. government does its part to protect the source of foods by inspecting and grading them at the source to ensure they are pure, wholesome, and safe to eat. Food must be purchased from legal, approved, and reputable suppliers.

When receiving food during a delivery, trained staff supervised by management have a significant opportunity to safeguard the restaurant from a food-borne illness outbreak and financial loss. Some foods are not allowed to be used if they are not pasteurized, are not of the correct grade, are mislabeled, or missing the proper identification tags. Food can become contaminated at the processing plant or in transit through mishandling or temperature abuse and should therefore be rejected.

Key Terms

Keep an eye out for these essential topics:

- Wholesome
- Approved suppliers
- USDA Inspection stamp
- Grading
- Use-by dates
- Expiration dates
- Recalls
- Shellstock identification tag
- Key drop delivery

Objectives

After working through this chapter, you should be able to explain the following to friends and family:

- Describe the difference between U.S. Food Law and the FDA Food Code
- Explain USDA inspection and grading
- Appreciate the importance of good receiving practices
- Learn how to measure food temperature at receiving
- Explore the difference between acceptable foods and non acceptable foods
- Understand the required receiving temperatures

Adriana,
Nutrition Specialist

Adriana was new to the elementary school kitchen but had several years of experience working in a traditional restaurant and had also earned her Food Safety Manager certification. She really loved the new job, its benefits, and seeing the young children all day. But there was one thing Adriana saw that she did not like! In the dry storage room, she saw several boxes sitting directly on the floor.

Adriana remembered from training for the certification exam that food should never be stored directly on the floor. There are a few exceptions, like packaged water bottles, but large cardboard boxes, each filled with several cereal boxes, was not one of those exceptions.

When working on reorganizing the storage space to get the boxes up onto the bottom shelving, which was the correct six inches (152 mm) off the floor, she was reminded why food should never be stored on the floor. Total infestation! The bottom box in the back, which had apparently been there for a while, had a large hole chewed out of it by what must have been a well-fed rat. Luckily she did not see the rodents themselves, but it was still very unsettling. The school had to throw out all the cereal in the boxes on the floor and call a pest control operator to deal with the problem. Because, in addition to ruining food, the germs and fecal waste can contaminate food contact surfaces all around the kitchen.

Everyone still talks about how Adriana used her superpowers to uncover the rodent problem. But they all know it was actually her training and certification!

Food Sources

The source of food, or where it is purchased from, is vital for many reasons; preventing contamination is at the top of the list. Along a food's path from the field to the food operation's receiving area are innumerable ways that contamination can occur. From breeding, food, or farm equipment, pathogenic microorganisms may be present in living animals. Pathogenic or chemical hazards may be present in the environment from water, soils, or fertilizers, affecting both animals and crops. Closer to delivery, additional hazards present themselves, including damage from mishandling, refrigeration failure, pests, and chemical or physical contamination. Last but not least, there are many laws regulating the source of many foods. Therefore it is vital to understand the source of food purchased for a food operation and to use **approved suppliers** with a good reputation.

For food operations serving **highly susceptible populations** (HSP) there are additional restrictions a food manager must consider when sourcing food and beverage products. For example, schools serving children under the age of 9 years old may not serve unpasteurized packaged juice.

U.S. Food Law Requirements

Aimed at protecting the consumer's health, safety, and economic resources, the FDA enforces its regulations and laws enacted by the U.S. Congress. One of the world's most extensive laws of its kind, the **Federal Food, Drug, and Cosmetic Act** is the primary food and drug law of the U.S.

According to the FDA, the law intends to assure the consumer that foods are pure, **wholesome**, safe to eat, and produced under sanitary conditions and that all labeling and packaging is truthful, informative, and not deceptive.

To comply with the U.S. Food Law, the source of food must:

3-201.11

- Comply with the law.

- Not be prepared in a private residence.

- Have package labeling in compliance with the law.

- Be from a supplier that properly freezes (and retains records) for fish intended to be eaten raw.

- Be from a supplier that meets specific whole-muscle, intact beef requirements.

- Be labeled appropriately for safe handling instructions for:
  1. Meat and poultry that is not an RTE Food.
  2. Eggs not treated to destroy all visible *salmonellae*.

FDA Food Code Requirements

The FDA Food Code is not federal law but becomes **legally binding** in states and jurisdictions that adopt it. The model Food Code is designed to align with federal food laws and regulations, meaning there should not be any contradictions.

The source of food must meet the following requirements to comply with the FDA Food Code:

3-201.13

Milk

must be purchased from sources that comply with Grade A Standards.

3-201.14

Fish

received for sale or service shall be:
1. Commercially and legally caught or harvested, or
2. Approved for sale or service

3-201.15

Molluscan Shellfish

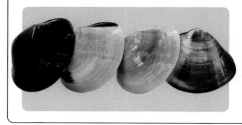

Interstate molluscan shellfish shipments must be from sources on the Interstate Certified Shellfish Shippers List. Recreationally caught molluscan shellfish may not be received for sale or service.

3-201.16

Mushrooms

Mushrooms picked in the wild shall not be offered for sale or service by a food establishment (some exceptions apply).

3-201.17

Game Animals

received for service shall be commercially raised for food. A food operation may not receive for sale or service any animal on the endangered species list.

Inspection and Grading

The USDA maintains two separate programs for inspecting and grading meat and poultry. **Inspection** for wholesomeness is mandatory and paid for by U.S. tax dollars. **Grading** for quality is voluntary and paid for by the producers/processors.

A purple **USDA inspection stamp** is added to raw meat, poultry, or packaged/processed meat that has passed USDA inspection. This indicates proper standards have been adhered to at the processing plant, and not that it is free of pathogens. The mark is put on the carcass and major cuts with a vegetable-based dye but may not appear on retail cuts. However,

Figure 1

the packaging label will have an inspection mark identifying the plant. Any meat or poultry product not inspected is considered adulterated and not legal to sell or purchase (see recall section later in this chapter).

Meat

Poultry

U.S.
INSPECTED
AND PASSED BY
DEPARTMENT OF
AGRICULTURE
EST.38

Processed

The FDA periodically inspects producers of FDA-regulated food products. The result is a written report at the conclusion of the inspection and does not include stamps.

Use-by Dates

Most **sell-by**, **use-by dates**, and **expiration dates** are added to food packages voluntarily by the manufacturer. These dates are added for various reasons, and may not technically be spoiled when the indicated date has passed. However, TCS Foods must be consumed or discarded by the expiration date unless the product has been frozen. Additionally, a food establishment's date markings on storage containers may not exceed the manufacturer's use-by date.

Figure 2

Figure 3

Annex 3, Page 127

From the FDA Food Code:

Although most use-by and sell-by dates are not enforceable by regulators, the manufacturer's use-by date is its recommendation for using the product while its quality is at its best. Although it is a guide for quality, it could be based on food safety reasons. It is recommended that food establishments consider the manufacturer's information as good guidance to follow to maintain the quality (taste, smell, and appearance) and salability of the product. If the product becomes inferior quality-wise due to time in storage, it is possible that safety concerns are not far behind.

Recalls and Public & Health Alerts

A food recall is the removal or correction of a marketed product that contains contaminants, unidentified ingredients, is mislabeled, or is in violation of the law. Food that has been recalled should not be received or used in a food operation. Food found to be recalled after receipt should be discarded or

Figure 4

clearly labeled **"DO NOT USE/ DO NOT DISCARD"** and held away from other foods and related supplies/equipment, in a secure location. Note that in some cases recalled products need to be held, rather than discarded, to meet the supplier's requirement of receiving a refund or replacement product.

2021 USDA recall stats:
- Total Recalls: 47
- Number of Pounds Recalled: 15,501,273

Examples of USDA recalls:
- Recalled Frozen Beef Products Due to Misbranding and Undeclared Allergens
- Recalled RTE Food Due to Possible Listeria Contamination
- Recalled Meat Pizza Products Produced Without Benefit of Inspection

Recall Websites

Distributors will often notify their customers of recalls, but food managers should also monitor the USDA and FDA recall sites:

- USDA: https://www.fsis.usda.gov/recalls
- FDA: https://www.fda.gov/safety/recalls-market-withdrawals-safety-alerts

Recall Classifications

Both the FDA and USDA classify recalls based on the potential to affect human health, with Class I being the most dangerous and therefore most important to keep track of and watch for during receiving.

- **Class I-High or Medium Risk**
  This is a health hazard situation where there is a reasonable probability that the use of the product will cause serious, adverse health consequences or death.

- **Class II-Low Risk**
  This is a health hazard situation where there is a remote probability of adverse health consequences from the use of the product.

- **Class III-Marginal Risk**
  This is a situation where the use of the product will not cause adverse health consequences.

Receiving

3-202.11

In a food operation, receiving is the initial point of entry for all deliveries of food and supplies. The receiving process is not just a physical task of moving heavy boxes to storage. First, trained staff must carefully inspect all food to avoid admitting contaminated food onto the premises, which can lead to foodborne illness or contaminate other foods. Safety is a high priority, but additional expenses and staff time are also at stake if contaminated or soiled products need to be held separately and an exchange coordinated with the supplier. By contrast, when products are rejected at receiving, they are not paid for, nor are they the food operation's responsibility.

Figure 4

Managers should coordinate delivery schedules with suppliers and ensure proper staffing for receiving activities. To run a smooth operation and to be ready for an inspection, anyone receiving food products must be familiar with these FDA receiving requirements:

> Packaging and Labeling   Temperature   Eggs and milk products   Ice

> Molluscan shellfish   Use-by dates   Recalls   Receiving logs

To highlight the importance of this aspect of the flow of food, here are examples of foodborne illnesses that are associated with poor receiving practices.

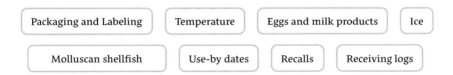

Scombrotoxin	*check the temperature at receiving*

Primarily associated with tuna fish, mahi-mahi, blue fish, anchovies bonito, mackerel, and cheese.

Aflatoxin	*check the condition at receiving*

Corn and corn products, peanuts and peanut products, cottonseed, milk, and tree nuts such as Brazil nuts, pecans, pistachio nuts, and walnuts. Other grains and nuts are susceptible but less prone to contamination.

Botulism Toxin	*check packaging condition at receiving*

Compromised reduced oxygen packaging (ROP) may allow botulism toxin to form.

Key Drop Delivery

While most deliveries are made during a food operation's normal business hours, there are situations where that is not possible. In these cases, a **key drop delivery** method is used, where a distributor is provided after-hours access using a key or code. Rather than just delivering the products to the receiving area, the delivery driver(s) places the products in coolers, freezers, and dry storage. When the operation is next open, the products are inspected per the requirements and best practices outlined in this chapter. Rejected products are labeled and set aside or discarded as instructed by the distributor.

Consider the following when contracting with key drop distributors:

- Approved and reputable
- Staff trained to properly store and label products
- Products are wholesome and honestly represented
- Rejected products will be removed/replaced in a timely manner

2-103.11(F)
Annex 3, Page 17

Packaging

When receiving deliveries, inspect food packages to ensure they are in good condition and protect the integrity of the contents to avoid adulteration or potential contamination. Grounds for rejection include dents, tears, cuts, stains, leaking liquids, and signs of insects or rodent damage. Defects may not be obvious, especially with low-acid canned foods. Close inspection may reveal dents, seam defects, and swelling, necessitating those products be rejected or returned and not offered for sale or consumption.

3-202.15

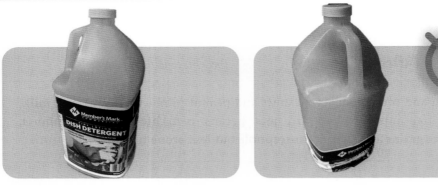

Figure 5   Figure 6

Labeling

Products should be received with intact labels which comply with the law. Proper labels will, for example, indicate if products have expired, been pasteurized, or contain allergens. Products missing labels should be rejected as part of a food defense program to limit possible intentional contamination.

Juice products that have not been pasteurized must contain the following warning on the label and may not be served to HSP consumers:

WARNING: This product has not been pasteurized and, therefore, may contain harmful bacteria that can cause illness in children, the elderly, and persons with weakened immune systems.

Temperature

3-202.11

Properly refrigerated foods within their use-by date prevent or limit the growth of most types of pathogens from multiplying to unsafe levels. The Food Code requires certain foods to be received at specified temperatures, or they must be rejected. The following foods must be received at the specified temperatures:

Refrigerated TCS Foods	41°F (5°C) or below
Raw eggs	45°F (7°C) or below
Milk	45°F (7°C) or below, cool to 41 < 4 hour
Shucked shellfish	45°F (7°C), cool to 41 < 4 hours (non-living product)
Shellstock	45°F (7°C), (internal 50F), cool to 41 < 4 hours (living product)

Cooked TCS Foods received hot for service	135°F (57°C) or above
Foods labeled and shipped frozen	Frozen

TCS foods (e.g., raw meats, cut tomato/melon/leafy greens) should be delivered to a food establishment in a refrigerated truck for quality and safety, free of evidence of previous temperature abuse. For example, products with a significant amount of ice crystals are a sign that the product was partially or fully thawed previously and should therefore be rejected.

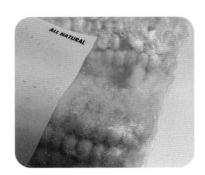

Figure 7

Eggs

Whole raw eggs must be received clean, sound, and free of damage. Egg products (i.e., eggs removed from their shells) shall be pasteurized and Grade B.

3-202.13

What are egg products?

The term "egg products" refers to eggs that are removed from their shells for processing, which includes breaking eggs, filtering, mixing, stabilizing, blending, pasteurizing, cooling, freezing, drying, and packaging. This is done at plants inspected by the United States Department of Agriculture (USDA).

3-202.14

Reasons to reject eggs at receiving:

- Restricted egg, e.g. incubator reject, check, or leaking egg
- Broken shell or crack, but membrane intact and not leaking
- Adhering dirt, foreign material, or prominent stains
- Inedible due to rot, sour eggs, green whites, incubation
- Liquid, frozen eggs, dried eggs, and egg products are not pasteurized
- Raw eggs not delivered in refrigerated equipment
- Above maximum receiving temperature of 45°F (7°C)

Damaged eggs allow bacteria to enter, where it can grow particularly well to dangerous levels. They must never be used for food.

Egg products must be pasteurized due to the exceptional bacterial growth potential. This involves a heat process that kills or inactivates harmful pathogens. Freezing or drying is not an acceptable alternative to pasteurization as neither is as thorough at killing bacteria.

Milk

3-202.14

Fluid and dry milk and milk products shall be received pasteurized, Grade A. Frozen milk products and ice cream shall be pasteurized. Cheese shall be pasteurized, with some exceptions.

Reasons to reject milk or milk products at receiving:

- Leaking / damaged packaging

- Frozen products not frozen

- Not labeled as pasteurized

- Adhering dirt, foreign material, or prominent stains

- Above maximum receiving temperature of 45°F (7°C)

Figure 8

Ice

3-202.16

When ice is used as a food or a cooling medium it shall be made from drinking (potable) water. As previously mentioned, freezing does not ensure the destruction of all bacteria, so any ice used in a food operation must be made using potable water.

Figure 9

> **KEY TERM**
>
> **Molluscan shellfish** means any edible species of fresh or frozen oysters, clams, mussels, and scallops or edible portions thereof, except when the scallop product consists only of the shucked adductor muscle.
>
> Molluscan shellfish includes shellstock, shucked shellfish and in-shell products.

Molluscan Shellfish

3-202.18

Molluscan Shellfish must be received in nonreturnable packages or containers bearing a **shellstock identification tag** or label including:

Dealer information:

- Source, affixed by dealer
- Date marking:
  - Capacity of 0.5 gallon (1.89 L) or less: "sell by" or "best if used by" date
  - Capacity of 0.5 gallon (1.89 L) or more: date shucked

Harvester information:

- Harvester's identification number
- Date of harvesting
- The type and quantity of shellfish
- The following statement in bold, capitalized type:
  THIS TAG IS REQUIRED TO BE ATTACHED UNTIL CONTAINER IS EMPTY OR RETAGGED AND THEREAFTER KEPT ON FILE FOR 90 DAYS

3-203.11

When a food establishment receives mollusan shellfish, it shall not be removed from the container in which they are received other than immediately before sale or preparation for service

A package of raw molluscan shellfish that is missing a label, or has an incomplete label, is subject to a hold order or seizure and destruction. Therefore, these items should be rejected during receiving.

3-203.12

Tags, labels, or invoices must be kept on file for 90 days after the last mollusan shellfish is sold or served to trace it back to its original source in case of a foodborne illness outbreak. This timeframe, as listed below, accounts for the incubation and discovery of the typical worst-case virus senario, hepatitis A.

Why 90 days?

Shelf-life of the product	14 days
Incubation period	56 days
Medical diagnosis and confirmation	5 days
Reporting	5 days
Epidemiological investigation	10 days
Total:	90 days

Freezing shellstock effectively stops the clock on the shelf-life. However, due to the change in texture and appearance shellstock is rarely frozen at a food establishment. By contrast, commercially frozen shellstock retain product quality due to the rapid freezing process.

3-202.17

Reasons to reject molluscan shellfish:

- Significant dead shellfish
- No open or badly broken shells
- Dirty and/or off odor smells
- Above maximum receiving temperature of 45°F (7°C)
- Missing or incomplete tag

Finfish

Due to water contaminants in specific locations or temperature abuse, *scombrotoxin* (histamine) toxin may be found in some finfish. This toxin is not eliminated by cooking. Therefore, using an approved reputable source and strict temperature control during receiving is critical.

Inspections

Food should be carefully inspected during delivery to ensure both quantity, quality, and temperature when appropriate. The inspection should be carried out by trained staff. The process should never be rushed, even if the delivery driver is in a hurry or the kitchen is unusually busy.

Checking Temperatures

Foods that are required to be received at minimum /maximum temperatures must be checked during receiving. When possible, internal temperatures should be checked. This involves unwrapping meats and opening packaged foods. However, reduced oxygen packaging (ROP), such as packaged bacon, cannot be opened, as it will affect the shelf-life and the potential for contamination. Additionally, fresh produce is not cut or prodded for similar reasons. Other foods like can/jar goods, spices, dry products, do not require a temperature check but are still inspected for package integrity and wholesomeness.

Inspecting for Quality

Using the information previously discussed in this chapter, a visual inspection should be made to assess: cleanliness, color, texture, odor, condition, and packaging. Below are several contrasting examples between an acceptable item and one that should be rejected at receiving.

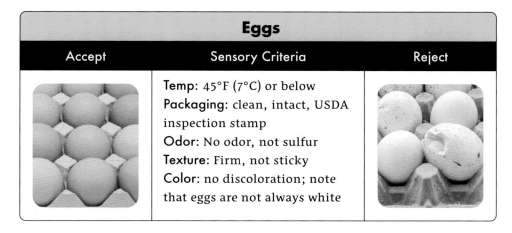

Meat – beef, pork, lamb		
Accept	**Sensory Criteria**	**Reject**
	Temp: 41°F (5°C) **Packaging:** clean, intact, USDA inspection stamp **Odor:** No odor, not sour **Texture:** Firm, not slimy **Color:** Beef: *bright cherry red* ROP beef: *purple* Lamb: *light red* Pork: *light pink*	

Poultry – chicken, duck, turkey, goose		
Accept	**Sensory Criteria**	**Reject**
	Temp: 41°F (5°C) or below **Packaging:** clean, intact, USDA inspection stamp **Odor:** No odor, not pungent **Texture:** Firm, not sticky **Color:** no discoloration, such as green or purple at the neck or dark wing tips	

Eggs		
Accept	**Sensory Criteria**	**Reject**
	Temp: 45°F (7°C) or below **Packaging:** clean, intact, USDA inspection stamp **Odor:** No odor, not sulfur **Texture:** Firm, not sticky **Color:** no discoloration; note that eggs are not always white	

Annex 3, 3-202.11

Annex 3, 3-202.13

3-202.14(B)

Milk

Accept	Sensory Criteria	Reject
	Temp: 45°F (7°C) or below, Cool to 41°F (5°C) within four hours **Packaging:** clean, intact, and labeled as Grade A, Pasteurized **Color/Odor:** White/Not sour **Texture:** Smooth, no curdling	

3-202.14(D)

Dairy Products – cheese, sour cream, butter, yogurt

Accept	Sensory Criteria	Reject
	Temp: 41°F (5°C) or below **Packaging:** clean, intact, and labeled as pasteurized (with some exceptions) **Odor:** Varies, not pungent **Texture:** Varies, not spoiled **Color:** Varies, not moldy	

Fresh produce – fresh fruits and vegetables

Accept	Sensory Criteria	Reject
	Temp: Varies - ambient or 41°F (5°C) or below **Packaging:** clean, intact, free of pests or related damage **Odor:** Varies, not pungent **Texture:** Varies, no signs of decay-darkened or slimy **Color:** Varies, fresh/crisp	

3-202.11(E)
3-202.14(C)

Frozen TCS Foods – Mashed potatoes, pizza, ice cream, etc.

Accept	Sensory Criteria	Reject
	Temp: 0°F (-18°C) or below, no signs of temperature abuse **Packaging:** clean, intact, no stains, has use-by date **Odor:** None **Texture:** No ice crystals **Ice Cream:** must be pasteurized	

Annex 5, Page 16

Fresh Finfish – all fish species excluding molluscan shellfish

Accept	Sensory Criteria	Reject
	**Temp:** 41°F (5°C) or below **Packaging:** clean, intact - when ice-packed; ice must be crushed, self-draining **Odor:** Mild fish smell, not strong fishy or ammonia **Texture:** Firm flesh, resilient **Eyes:** Clear, not cloudy/sunken	

3-202.18
3-203.11(D)
3-203.12(C)(2)

Shucked Shellfish – clams, oysters, mussels, and scallops

Accept	Sensory Criteria	Reject
	**Temp:** 45°F (7°C) or below, Cool to 41°F (5°C) within four hours **Packaging:** clean, intact non-returnable case with proper ID label and sell-by date **Odor:** Mild seafood smell, not strong fishy, Firm flesh, resilient	

3-202.17
3-203.11
3-203.12

Shellstock – live clams, oysters, mussels, and scallops

Accept	Sensory Criteria	Reject
	**Temp:** 50°F (10°C) or below, delivery truck air at 45°F (7°C) **Packaging:** clean, intact non-returnable case with proper ID tag (save tag for 90 days) **Odor:** Mild seafood smell, not strong fishy **Shells:** Clean, Closed, unbroken **Condition:** received alive	

Annex 6, Page 2

ROP Foods

Accept	Sensory Criteria	Reject
	**Temp:** 41°F (5°C) or below **Packaging:** clean, intact, use-by-date on the label **Odor:** None	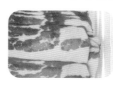

3-202.11

Annex 3, 3-201.12

Annex 3, 3-201.15

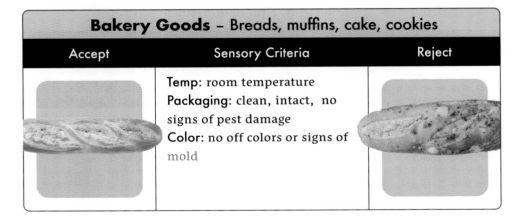

Crustaceans – Crab, shrimp, lobster

Accept	Sensory Criteria	Reject
	Temp: 41°F (5°C) or below **Packaging:** clean, intact **Odor:** Mild seafood smell, not strong fishy **Shells:** Clean, unbroken **Condition:** received alive	

Canned Food

Accept	Sensory Criteria	Reject
	Temp: room temperature **Packaging:** clean, no dents or leaks, no swelling, label intact, no pest droppings **Odor:** None	

Bakery Goods – Breads, muffins, cake, cookies

Accept	Sensory Criteria	Reject
	Temp: room temperature **Packaging:** clean, intact, no signs of pest damage **Color:** no off colors or signs of mold	

Health Inspector Visit – Receiving

Food managers should consider what the health inspector will be looking for when visiting during the receiving process. If an official inspection does not overlap the receiving process, the person in charge will likely be asked questions about the receiving process and ask to see related logs. Both purchase and receiving records may be needed for traceback by officials if a foodborne illness outbreak occurs.

Annex 5, Page 16

From the FDA Food Code:

If food is being delivered during the inspection, inspectors should:

- Verify internal product temperatures

- Examine package integrity upon delivery

- Look for signs of temperature abuse (e.g., large ice crystals in the packages of frozen products)

- Examine delivery truck and products for potential for cross-contamination

- Observe the food establishment's behaviors and practices as they relate to the establishment's control of contamination and holding and cooling temperatures of received products

- Review receiving logs and other documents, product labels, and food products to ensure that foods are received from regulated food processing plants (no foods prepared at home) and at the proper temperature.

Inspectors should look to see that raw animal foods and ready-to-eat foods are separated during receiving, storage, and preparation.

Receiving Checklist

Managers can create checklists to train and remind staff of essential steps and controls required during receiving. Keeping records is an important aspect of keeping food safe and reinforcing accountability.

Summary

The theme of this chapter is to understand the source of foods and the proper receiving practices. Management often orders products to be delivered and is responsible for understanding the associated laws and best practices. Properly trained staff who take their time to inspect food during deliveries will be effective in preventing unwanted products from entering the facility. Suitable receiving methods include a sensory inspection, looking for discoloration, smelling for off odors, touching for texture, and measuring for required temperatures.

When receiving TCS Foods it is imperative they are not time and/or temperature abused. They should be delivered in a refrigerated truck and their temperatures checked. Signs of previous temperature abuse should also be assessed. Most TCS foods are to be delivered at 41°F (5°C) or below with some exceptions, like whole eggs may be received at 45°F (7°C) or below. Measurements must be logged to ensure proper food safety controls are being followed.

- The U.S. Food Law are federal laws passed by Congress.
- The FDA Food Code is not law until/unless adopted by a state, county, city, or tribal authority.
- Good receiving practices can prevent foodborne illness and financial loss.
- Use the appropriate method to measure the temperature of food at delivery:
    - Meat: probe inserted into the thickest part
    - ROP: probe placed between two packages, not penetrating the packaging
    - Packaged foods: remove lid and insert the probe
    - Fruits and vegetables: measure surface temp with infrared, not penetrating product
- Staff look for discoloration, smell for off odors, touch for texture, and measure for required temperatures.
- Shucked shellfish, shellstock, and finfish must be received clean, without broken shells, alive (shellstock), and with proper labeling and/or identification tags.

The Student's Workbook

As assigned by your instructor, use the separate Student's Workbook to work independently or in groups. Activities for this week's chapter include:

- Create a Receiving criteria poster
- Voting on the best (and completely accurate) poster in the class
- Watch the video and reflect
- Discuss the risks of each ingredient in the broccoli & cheddar soup recipe
- Make a list of equipment needed
- Produce the recipe
- Review the cleaning and sanitizing checklist
- Fill out the recipe and cost form
- End of chapter review video

Use these questions to check your knowledge of the material in this chapter. *Your instructor has the answers.*

1 The name of the federal U.S. Food Law is _____.

a. FDA Food Code

b. Federal Food, Drug, and Cosmetic Act

c. USDA Food Law

d. American Food and Drug Act

2 Which is not a source requirement according to the U.S. Food Law?

a. In packages weighing less than 50 pounds

b. Comply with law

c. Be labeled appropriately

d. Not prepared in a private residence

3 Which is not voluntary?

a. Use-by date

b. Expiration date

c. USDA inspection

d. USDA grading system

4 Which foodborne illness is not associated with poor receiving practices?

a. Scombrotoxin

b. Aflatoxin

c. Norovirus

d. Botulism Toxin

5 Which TCS food may be received at 45°F (7°C) or below?

a. Raw eggs

b. Vegetables

c. Meat

d. Poultry

6 Which is a sign of previous temperature abuse?

a. Missing label

b. Dirty packaging

c. Past use-by-date

d. Ice crystals

7 Which is not a reason to reject whole raw eggs?

a. Leaking

b. Broken shells

c. Shells not white

d. Stained shells

8 Which is not required to be pasteurized?

a. Fresh produce

b. Milk

c. Eggs

d. Yogurt

Chapter 7

Storage

Introduction

Storage is usually the next stop for food once it has been received within a food operation. The big things to understand are proper containers, labeling, date marking, rotation, temperature, and contamination control. Food operations have three primary types of food storage spaces: dry, refrigerated, and frozen.

These spaces must be well maintained and monitored to ensure food is fresh, free of contaminants, and kept at the proper temperatures. Food that becomes expired, contaminated, or time/temperature abused in storage must be discarded. Failure to properly manage stored food often leads to foodborne illness.

Since food storage spaces are often out of sight, they may also be out of mind. Meaning that, since they are not used as often as other spaces, they could be overlooked. Therefore, a food manager must develop staff training, procedures, and logs to ensure storage spaces are in tip-top shape. Doing so will also help facilitate a smooth inspection by the health department.

Key Terms

Keep an eye out for these essential topics:

- Walk-in cooler
- Date marking
- First-in, First-out (FIFO) method
- Reduced Oxygen Packaging (ROP) Foods
- Reconditioned
- Comminuted
- Condensate
- Working containers

Objectives

After working through this chapter, you should be able to explain the following to friends and family:

- Describe the types of food storage spaces
- Understand the vertical food storage requirements
- Learn about the importance of date marking
- Describe the purpose of first-in, first-out (FIFO)
- Understand what cannot be placed in a food storage space
- Explain the temperature requirements for stored food

Kenedy, Food Safety Manager

Kenedy is the food safety manager of a popular family-style Italian restaurant in Minneapolis. They use a method to ensure active managerial control over the food operation: dividing some routine tasks among staff, giving them responsibility, and spreading accountability. In this way, all the crucial things that keep food safe and that the inspector looks for are not all performed by one person, who can more easily forget one to two items from time to time. However, even one person can slip up occasionally, which is exactly what happened last week.

It was a busy Wednesday lunch, which was unusual, and the dairy delivery had just arrived. Kenedy has traditionally scheduled the dairy delivery for this day because it is usually not too busy. This week's delivery time also sets them up with dairy products that will last them through the high-volume weekend. Well, the person in charge of dairy deliveries was so busy they decided not to immediately follow the First-In, First-Out (FIFO) storage method. They figured it could not hurt to wait an hour and move everything around them. So they simply placed all the milk in the walk-in cooler in front of the older milk.

Fast forward to the end of the rush that lasted longer than expected. Everyone was exhausted, and there was just enough time to clean and sanitize before the staff shift change. The milk was forgotten and never rotated. Fast forward, once more, to the middle of a busy weekend, and the problem was discovered! All the milk in the back had spoiled. In fact, it looked more like yogurt than milk. Since it was the weekend, they could not call their distributor and had to send someone with a truck to the nearby grocery store to buy more milk.

This mistake cost the restaurant a lot of money, from discarding milk to buying new milk at the higher grocery-store prices, and the time it took the person sent for milk. Not to mention the reputation problem if the milk was accidentally used or if a surprise inspection would have occurred.

Kenedy managed the issue and now references it often as a training example during new hire orientations.

Types of Storage

A full-service food operation has several types of storage, each with a specific purpose and temperature requirement. This section reviews the main types of storage in the back-of-house to establish the proper terminology.

These rooms or areas have several requirements in common, such as:

- Adequate size for the product stored, staff movement, and cleaning
- Conveniently located for deliveries and preparation access
- Controlled access - limited to those with a legitimate need to enter
- Proper lighting levels for safety and tasks required
- Easy to clean, with products stored 6 inches (15 cm) above the floor
- Free of pests and related activities (gnawing, droppings)
- Mechanically ventilated per building codes and energy efficient

☑ At the request of a health inspector, a manager must be able to state the required temperatures for the safe refrigerated storage of time/temperature control for safety (TCS) food.

Dry Storage

Dry storage is meant explicitly for **single-service** items and packaged food that is not time/temperature control for safety (TCS) food. This includes canned goods, dried goods, tableware, carry-out utensils, straws, containers, placemats, stirrers, tooth-picks, etc.

The space must be clean, dry, and located away from sources of dust, splashes, and other contaminants. The room should not be used for other purposes or shared with a stairwell or hallway. A dry storage room is enclosed with standard walls and often has a locking door to control access.

6-201.16

Figure 1

Refrigerated Storage

3-501.12

 Temp: 41°F (5°C) or below

The primary refrigerated storage in most kitchens is the **walk-in cooler**. Time/temperature control for safety (TCS) foods are required to be held at this temperature.

Annex 3, Page 164

This is a large enclosed space built similar to a bank vault, except the thick solid steel walls/floor/ceiling and door are filled with insulation and covered with durable, easy-to-clean metal or plastic. The walk-in unit has a dedicated cooling unit, similar to a residential refrigerator but much more powerful. It also has integrated lighting and a temperature measurement system to easily monitor the internal ambient air temperature and humidity without opening the door.

Temperature readings must be accurate to +/- 3°F (+/- 1.5°C.) Some contemporary models connect to WiFi and automatically record temperature logs.

The temperature of refrigerated foods should be checked and logged regularly, and corrective action should be taken when necessary. TCS foods are ideally positioned away from the cooler door to minimize potential temperature

Figure 2

abuse. The cooler door may be opened and closed several times during the day in a busy operation. Adding "cold curtains" or "plastic strip curtains" to the door can help minimize the cold air that escapes when the cooler door is opened.

Frozen Storage

3-501.11

 Temp: 0°F (-18°C) or below

A walk-in freezer has all the characteristics described for the walk-in cooler, except the walls/floor/ceiling and door are often thick enough to insulate better given the lower temperature. Walk-in freezers are designed to enter a defrost cycle on a schedule to minimize frost build-up and maintain efficiency. Some freezers may need to be manually defrosted by unplugging and removing their contents.

A freezer must be capable of keeping frozen foods frozen. Signs of temperature abuse, meaning food has partially thawed previously, include malformed products, ice crystals, and leaking.

Figure 3

Garbage Storage

Figure 4

A separate area must be designated for garbage/refuse/waste, recycling, empty product containers, and returnables. These items are unclean and may attract pests and rodents, creating the potential for cross-contamination with food. Therefore, food products, equipment, single-service items, single-use items, and related supplies may not be stored adjacent to the designated garbage storage area. The FDA Food Code also requires that this space be located to allow cleaning adjacent areas and to preclude the creation of a nuisance.

5-501.10 - 13

Preventing Contamination

When food is not stored correctly, it can become contaminated and lead to foodborne illness. As covered in previous chapters, food contamination can range from large physical objects to invisible (to the naked eye) microorganisms.

Here are some examples of how poor storage practices can lead to contamination:

- Air quality: poor ventilation, unfiltered air, leaky unit
- Moisture: uncontrolled humidity, leaking condensate or plumbing
- Misuse: stored trash, kitchen equipment, smoking/vaping, taking breaks, intimacy
- Cleanliness: build-up of dirt and debris, filthy hands, soiled shoes, spills

Additionally, to prevent intentional contamination, a food manager must ensure that:

- Persons unnecessary to the food establishment operation are not allowed in the food storage areas – except for brief authorized tours/visits where food and equipment are reasonably protected

2-103.11(B)

- Employees and other persons such as delivery and maintenance persons and pesticide applicators entering the food storage areas comply with this Code

2-103.11(C)

Food Storage Requirements

The FDA Food Code provides the following list outlining specific steps a food operation must comply with to protect stored food from contamination.

3-305.11

Food must be stored:

- In a clean, dry location
- Where it is not exposed to splash, dust, or other contamination
- At least 6 inches (15 cm) above the floor, except:
  Food in packages and **working containers** may be stored less than 6 inches (15 cm) above the floor on case lot handling equipment.
- Pressurized beverage containers, cased food in waterproof containers (e.g., bottles or cans) and milk containers in plastic crates may be stored on a clean floor that is not exposed to floor moisture.

Figure 5

3-305.12

Food is prohibited from being stored:

- In locker rooms
- In toilet rooms
- In dressing rooms
- In garbage rooms
- In mechanical rooms
- Under sewer lines that are not shielded to intercept potential drips
- Under leaking water lines, including leaking automatic fire sprinkler heads, or under lines on which water has condensed
- Under open stairwells
- Under other sources of contamination

KEY TERM

Condensate or Condensed water When there is a significant temperature difference between the air in a room (e.g., warm) and the contents of a pipe (e.g., cold) in the ceiling space of the room, the moisture in the warm air condenses on the surface of the pipe. This liquid can pool and begin to drip.

Food Separation Requirements

In addition to where food may be stored, the FDA also specifies how it is to be stored to prevent food and ingredient contamination. This includes the proper separation of packaged and unpackaged foods.

Protect stored food from cross-contamination by separating raw animal foods from:

3-302.11

- Raw ready-to-eat (RTE) food, including other raw animal food such as fish for sushi or molluscan shellfish, or other raw ready-to-eat (RTE) food such as fruits and vegetables
- Cooked ready-to-eat (RTE) food
- Fruits and vegetables before they are washed
- Frozen, commercially processed, and packaged raw animal food may be stored or displayed with or above frozen, commercially processed and packaged, ready-to-eat (RTE) food

Except for raw poultry or fish delivered in packed ice, packaged food may not be stored in direct contact with ice if the packaging is subject to water entry, such as a cardboard box.

Time/temperature control for safety (TCS) foods should be covered or packaged while in cold storage.

Vertical Storage Order

In addition to the general concept of storing food separately, the position of food stored above/below other foods must be considered.

Food managers must train their staff to prevent cross-contamination of stored food by never positioning raw animal foods above ready-to-eat (RTE) foods. Additionally, raw animal foods with a higher required internal cook temperature (to effectively kill pathogens) may not be stored above other raw animal foods with a lower required internal cook temperature.

Raw animal foods with a higher required internal cook temperature must be kept below or separate from foods with a lower internal cook temperature. Note that any of these items may be stored at the same level as long as there is adequate horizontal separation to prevent cross-contamination. As an exception, the FDA does not restrict storage separation for frozen, commercially packaged RTE foods and raw animal foods.

Vertical Storage Order Visualized

The following table explains the vertical position requirements when foods are stored above/below other foods.

Ready-to-eat foods must never be stored below raw animal foods.

Annex 3, 3-302.11

Vertical order, top to bottom	Minimum internal cook temperature
Washed, cut tomatoes	Not applicable
Ready-to-eat food, fully cooked food, fresh produce	Not applicable
Seafood, eggs	145°F (63°C)
Intact & Non-intact meats, Beef, pork, veal, lamb	145°F (63°C)
Comminuted: Ground meat, ground fish	155°F (68°C)
Poultry	165°F (73°C)

KEY TERM Comminuted means reduced in size by chopping, flaking, grinding, or mincing, which includes gefilte fish (ground fish), gyros, ground beef, and sausage.

Two Contrasting Examples

Consider these two examples; one is an acceptable outcome and the other is not:

Internal cook temperatures

Raw pork: 145°F (63°C)

Raw poultry: 165°F (73°C)

Acceptable:

- Raw pork is stored above raw chicken
- The raw pork leaks onto the raw chicken
- Cross-contamination has occurred
- However, the raw chicken can be **reconditioned**
- Cook the chicken to the required 165°F (73°C)
- The pork pathogens effectively killed at 145°F (63°C)

Unacceptable:

- Raw chicken is stored above raw pork
- The raw chicken leaks onto the raw pork
- Cross-contamination has occurred
- The raw pork cannot be reconditioned
- Cook the pork to the required 145°F (63°C)
- The chicken pathogens have not been effectively killed
- The pork must be discarded

☑ Health inspectors are trained to look for proper storage of RTE and TCS foods. If contamination has occurred, they assess whether the food can be reconditioned or must be discarded.

Proper storage of raw animal food is not only a food safety issue, it is also an economic one. Discarding food purchased but not eaten by the consumer is one thing. But discarding food due to mistakes in the kitchen can eat into the business's profits. Poor management in this area can quickly escalate to the operation going out of business.

> **KEY TERM**
>
> Reconditioned means contaminated food can be made safe for consumption through proper cooking to kill or reduce harmful pathogens to safe levels. This may also include cutting away food mold as allowed in the FDA Food Code. Reconditioning is impossible for certain contaminants, such as chemical or allergen hazards.

Poisonous or Toxic Chemicals

7-201.11

Figure 6

The FDA Food Code requires that poisonous or toxic chemicals be stored in a separate room to prevent contamination of food, equipment, and food-related supplies. Specifically mentioned is separation by "partition," which means a wall in the building. These hazards may not be stored above food storage even when separated by a partition.

Only poisonous or toxic chemicals required in the food operation, such as disinfectant chemicals and pesticides, are allowed to be on the premises. By contrast, gasoline and paint thinner are forbidden. Strict access control must be in place to prevent access to customers and unnecessary staff.

Working containers used for storing poisonous or toxic materials such as cleaners and sanitizers taken from bulk supplies should be clearly and individually identified with the common name of the material.

☑ Health inspectors will look for properly stored poisonous and toxic chemicals as well as intact and legible manufacturer's labels.

Cleaning

Storage is sometimes overlooked in cleaning schedules since they are enclosed spaces that are out of sight. However, the Food Code requires that they be cleaned with a frequency so that soil residues are not accumulated. Additionally, garbage, soiled or contaminated equipment, or linens must not be brought into storage areas.

4-602.11(D)(5)

Storage cleaning guidelines:

- Clean whenever spills or contamination occur
- Regular cleaning to prevent soil residue
- Clean food storage containers when emptied
- Regular cleaning of equipment
    - ○ Shelving
    - ○ Dollies
    - ○ Carts
    - ○ Clean floors, moving items permitted to be on the floor

See chapter 10 for additional information on cleaning and sanitizing requirements and best practices within a food operation.

Product Controls

Keeping stored food safe involves a manager's thorough understanding of requirements and best practices for:

- Product containers
- Product labeling
- Date marking
- Product rotation
- Temperatures

Containers

Products are usually left in their original packaging for optimal identification, quality, freshness, and shelf-life. Once opened, the unused portion is stored in **food-approved containers** to maintain quality and freshness as long as possible. Containers often hold seasonings and other shelf-stable ingredients and are accessed when needed, in which case the containers are called **working containers**.

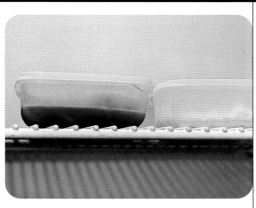

3-302.12

Figure 7

Container guidelines:

- Cleaned and sanitized for use
- Approved for food
- TCS foods must be covered
- Cleaned when emptied

Labeling

Certain foods or ingredients may be difficult to identify after they are removed from their original packaging. Additionally, products packaged in the food establishment for retail sale might accidentally receive the wrong label or be missing required information. This confusion may not just lead to a surprising or unpleasant-tasting meal; it could prove fatal if an allergen is involved in the mixup.

From the FDA Food Code:

Annex 3, Page 93

The mistaken use of food from unlabeled containers could result in chemical poisoning. For example, foodborne illness and death have resulted from the use of unlabeled salt, instead of sugar, in infant formula and special dietary foods. Liquid foods, such as oils, and granular foods that may resemble cleaning compounds are also of particular concern.

For Use On-site

3-302.12

When food or food ingredients are removed from their original packages, the FDA Food Code requires food-storage containers to be marked with the **common name of the food**. Examples of foods requiring this container marking requirement include cooking oils, flour, herbs, potato flakes, salt, spices, and sugar. Excluded are foods that are unmistakably recognized, like dry pasta.

Any products containing an ingredient or protein derived from any of the Big 9 allergen foods must name the food source on the label.

Labeling guidelines:

- Identified with the common name of food
- Except when contents are unmistakably recognized
- If contained, list the Big 9 food source
- Date marking as described in the next section

Figure 8

For Retail Sale

3-201.11
3-404.11

Some food establishments will package foods they have prepared for retail sale. They may have a "famous" pancake mix or wild rice soup they will prepare, package, label, and then sell to customers who bring the product home and prepare it for consumption later. Packaged foods must conform to labeling laws, including nutrition data and any major allergens that may be included.

Date Marking

3-501.17

Ready-to-eat TCS foods are presumed to have safe levels of bacteria when received and stored in a walk-in cooler. While TCS foods are properly refrigerated, bacterial growth is slowed but not completely stopped. Therefore, ready-to-eat TCS foods stored for extended periods can become contaminated and unsafe for consumption. In this case, the "time" portion of time/temperature for safety (TCS) is managed through **date marking** to prevent foodborne illness. Discard food found in unmarked containers.

3-501.19(C)(5)

Annex 3, Page 123

From the FDA Food Code:

Date marking requirements apply to containers of processed food that have been opened and to food prepared by a food establishment, in both cases if held for more than 24 hours, and while the food is under the control of the food establishment.

More than 24 hours

Once a ready-to-eat TCS food is prepared or a container opened, the storage container must be date marked if held for more than 24 hours. Date marking is not required if the prepared food or packaged contents are consumed within 24 hours.

Maximum of 7 days

Ready-to-eat TCS foods can be stored for a maximum of 7 days when refrigerated at 41°F (5°C) or below. The day of preparation is counted as day 1. If the stored food is not consumed or sold on day seven, it must be discarded. In any case, the date marking cannot exceed the use-by date on the original packaging.

Date Marking Systems

3-501.17(D)

The FDA offers some flexibility on how date marking is implemented. A food operation can either mark the date the food was prepared or the last day the food may be sold or consumed. Staff must be trained on the specific system used and made available to inspectors upon request.

Date marking system examples:

- Calendar dates
- Days of the week
- Color-coded marks,

    or

- Other effective means

Timeline examples:

- Less than 24 hours
  - RTE/TCS Food prepared
  - The entire portion was consumed the same day
  - No date marking required
- More than 24 hours
  - RTE/TCS Food prepared
  - A portion not consumed the same day
  - Date marking is required on the stored portion
  - The remaining portion is used within seven days
- More than seven days
  - RTE/TCS Food prepared
  - A portion not consumed the same day
  - Date marking is required on the stored portion
  - The remaining portion was not used within seven days

Combining Ingredients

3-501.17(B)(2)

When combining ingredients, the food shall retain the date marking of the earliest prepared food.

For example, if the following foods are combined:

- Hot dogs   Date marked: use-by 8/7 at 3:00 pm
- Macaroni noodles   Date marked: N/A
- Cheese   Date marked: use-by 8/5 at 11:00 am

The date marking on the new container must be: "**use-by 8/5 at 11:00 am**" to ensure the cheese does not become contaminated.

Date marking should never surpass the use-by or expiration date on any original packaging.

Product Rotation

Product rotation is vital for food quality, safety, and economic reasons.

When commercially packaged products surpass their labeled use-by or expiration date, they must be thrown out. Discarded food eats into an operation's profits. While this can result from certain menu items not being as popular, it more often stems from poor storage practices. These missteps can lead to more significant problems if expired food is unknowingly used and foodborne illness results.

The FDA Food Code recommends a product rotation method called **First-in, First-out** (FIFO). Employing this method, prepared or packaged food is organized based on date markings, use-by, and expiration dates. The earliest dates are positioned towards the front, making them more readily accessible. At the same time, the later dates are towards the back. This active managerial control method ensures that products closer to the expiration date are used first.

Annex 5, Page 31

When additional deliveries arrive or new foods are prepared, the FIFO method is used again. This process is particularly significant for RTE/TCS foods which, as discussed in the previous section, have a limited shelf-life.

Contaminated or Expired Food

Any packaged food that has become contaminated or expired must be discarded or held in a separate space as requested/required by the manufacturer/authorities if needed for a refund/replacement or health outbreak traceback. This requirement is similar to recalled products covered in the previous chapter.

3-701.11

Annex 3, Page 123

Annex 3, Page 152

6-404.11

The stored packages must be clearly labeled if the product is not immediately discarded. For example, if the product is being held for the supplier to retrieve, the label might read "DO NOT USE" and "RETURN TO SUPPLIER."

Figure 9

Storage Guidelines by Product

The information covered thus far in this chapter can be used to properly store most food items. This last section highlights the requirements of specific foods to reinforce those concepts.

Meat

Including cuts and steaks of beef, pork, veal, and lamb.

Status: time/temperature for safety food (TCS Food)

Time:

- Refrigerated:
  - Prepared or opened package: maximum 7 days
  - Reduced oxygen packaging (ROP): until the use-by date
- Frozen:
  - Varies: 3 – 12 months

Temperature:

- Refrigerated: 41°F (5°C) or below
- Frozen: Temperature required to keep meat frozen

Safety:

- Prevent cross-contamination:
  - Do not store above ready-to-eat (RTE) foods or seafood
  - Store separate from other raw animal foods
  - Keep in original packaging until use
  - To store unused raw portions:
  - Status: not an RTE food
  - Wrap in moisture-proof, airtight material, or
  - Store in a food-approved airtight container
  - Below RTE foods and seafood
  - Above other raw animal foods
- To store unused cooked portions:
  - Status: RTE food
  - Store in a food-approved container
  - Store above all non-RTE foods

Poultry

Status: time/temperature for safety food (TCS Food)

Time:

- Refrigerated:
  - ○ Prepared or opened package: maximum 7 days
  - ○ Reduced oxygen packaging (ROP): until the use-by date
- Frozen:
  - ○ Varies: 12 months

Temperature:

- Refrigerated: 41°F (5°C) or below
- Frozen: Temperature required to keep poultry frozen

Safety:

- Prevent cross-contamination:
  - ○ Do not store above ready-to-eat (RTE) foods, seafood, or meat
  - ○ Store separate from other raw animal foods
  - ○ Keep in original packaging until use
- To store unused raw portions:
  - ○ Status: not an RTE food
  - ○ Wrap in moisture-proof, airtight material, or
  - ○ Store in a food-approved airtight container
  - ○ Below all other raw and RTE foods
  - ○ Never above other raw animal foods
- To store unused cooked portions:
  - ○ Status: RTE food
  - ○ Store in a food-approved container
  - ○ Store above all non-RTE foods

Fish

Status: time/temperature for safety food (TCS Food) and Big 9 food allergen

Time:

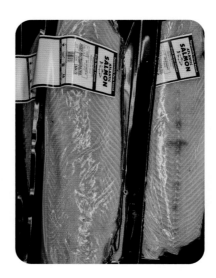

- Refrigerated:
  - Prepared or opened package: maximum 7 days
  - Reduced oxygen packaging (ROP): until the use-by date
- Frozen:
  - Varies: 3-12 months

Temperature:

- Refrigerated: 41°F (5°C) or below
- Frozen: Temperature required to keep fish frozen

Safety:

- Prevent cross-contamination:
  - Do not store above ready-to-eat (RTE) foods
  - Store separate from other raw animal foods
  - Keep in original packaging until use
- To store unused raw portions:
  - Status: not an RTE food
  - Wrap in moisture-proof, airtight material, or
  - Store in a food-approved airtight container
  - Below RTE foods
  - Above all other raw animal foods
- To store unused cooked portions:
  - Status: RTE food
  - Store in a food-approved container
  - Store above all non-RTE foods

Molluscan Shellfish

Status: time/temperature for safety food (TCS Food) and Big 9 food allergen

Time:

- Shucked shellfish (non-living):
  - ○ Prepared or opened package: maximum 7 days
  - ○ Reduced oxygen packaging (ROP): until the use-by date
- Shellstock (living): living shellfish can be stored up to 7 days when their shells are completely closed. This includes oysters, littlenecks, butter clams, and cockles. However, mussels can only be stored for three to four days.

Temperature:

- Refrigerated:
  - ○ Shucked shellfish held at 41°F (5°C) or below
  - ○ Shellstock at an air temperature of 41°F (5°C) or below

Safety:

- Shellfish must remain in the original container until prepared
- The shellfish identification tags must be kept on file for 90 days after last shellfish has been removed from the container.
- Prevent cross-contamination:
  - ○ Do not store above ready-to-eat (RTE) foods
  - ○ Store above or separate from other raw animal foods
- To store unused cooked portions:
  - ○ Status: RTE food
  - ○ Store in a food-approved container
  - ○ Store above all non-RTE foods
- Live shellfish may be stored in a display tank. If not labeled "for display only" a variance is required in order to prepare and serve to customers.

Eggs

Status: time/temperature for safety food (TCS Food) and Big 9 food allergen

Time:

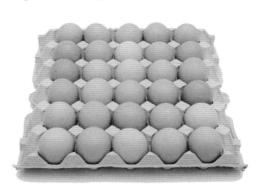

- Refrigerated:
  - Raw whole eggs: within 4-5 weeks of date on package
  - Prepared or egg products, maximum 7 days
  - Reduced oxygen packaging (ROP): until the use-by date
- Frozen: Egg products can be frozen for one year

3-501.16(B)

Temperature:

- Dry storage:
  - Dried egg products
- Refrigerated:
  - Whole eggs: ambient air temperature of 45°F (7°C) or below
  - Egg products: 41°F (5°C) or below
- Frozen:
  - Temperature required to keep frozen egg products frozen

Safety:

- Prevent cross-contamination:
  - Do not store above ready-to-eat (RTE) foods
  - Store above raw animal foods
  - Keep in original packaging
  - No need to "cool" shell eggs upon receipt
  - No need to wash before storing
  - Only remove anticipated number of eggs required from refrigeration
  - Maximize the circulation of cooled air in refrigeration units by separating flats, cases, and multiple cartons of eggs
- To store unused raw portions:
  - Status: not an RTE food
  - Store in a food-approved airtight container
  - Below RTE foods
  - Above all raw animal foods
- To store unused cooked portions:
  - Status: RTE food
  - Store in a food-approved container
  - Store above all non-RTE foods

Fresh Produce

Status: leafy greens, cut tomatoes, and cut melons are time/temperature for safety food (TCS Food)

Time:

- Refrigerated:
  - ○ TCS food, maximum 7 days
  - ○ Other items: varies

Temperature:

- Dry storage:
  - ○ Citrus fruit, eggplant, potatoes: 60°F – 70°F (16°C – 21°C)
- Refrigerated:
  - ○ TCS Food: 41°F (5°C) or below (cut leafy greens, cut tomatoes, cut melons)
  - ○ Other items: varies

Safety:

- If possible, separate fresh produce from other refrigerated foods using a separate set of storage racks or a separate cooler.
- Store all produce off the floor in covered containers.
- Do not use partially decayed or damaged tomatoes.
- If leafy greens are cut or chopped and not used within 24 hours, they must be date marked and used or sold within 7 days.
- Storing potatoes in the refrigerator can result in increased acrylamide during cooking. Therefore, store potatoes outside the refrigerator, preferably in a dark, cool place, such as a closet or a pantry, to prevent sprouting.
- Prevent cross-contamination:
  - ○ Do not store below raw animal food.
  - ○ Store washed, cut tomatoes above unwashed, uncut fresh produce.
  - ○ Keep in original packaging/containers, follow any storage and/or use-by instructions.
- To store unused cooked portions:
  - ○ Status: RTE food
  - ○ Store in a food-approved container.
  - ○ Store above all non-RTE foods.
- Temperature measurement of cut leafy greens:
  - ○ Insert a thin probe thermocouple in the thicker stem portions of the leaf.
  - ○ Use an infrared thermometer to measure the surface temperature of the leaves.
  - ○ Insert a thermometer stem or thermocouple probes between two sealed bags.

Annex 3, Page 85

Canned Goods

Time:

- Varies: adhere to the use-by date

Temperature:

- Dry storage: 60°F – 70°F (16°C – 21°C)

Safety:

- Discard cans with dents, swelling, or missing labels
- Watch for signs of pest or rodent activity such as gnawing or droppings
- Keep in original containers

Figure 10

Dry Foods

Time:

- Varies: adhere to the use-by date

Temperature:

- Dry storage: 60°F – 70°F (16°C – 21°C)

Safety:

- Discard dirty or stained packages
- Watch for signs of pest or rodent activity such as gnawing or droppings
- Keep in original packaging or use properly labeled working container

Figure 11

ROP Food

Reduced oxygen packaging (ROP) includes packaging options such as sous vide, modified atmosphere packaging (MAP), controlled atmosphere packaging (CAP), and cook-chill packaged foods. The Food Code requires a food establishment that packages TCS food using a ROP method to control the growth and toxin formation of *Clostridium botulinum* and the growth of *Listeria monocytogenes*.

Figure 12

3-502.12(D)(2)(e)

Commercially packaged	TCS Food packaged on premises
Time: ● Varies: adhere to the use-by date **Temperature:** ● Varies: adhere to manufacturer's instructions, for example: ○ Must be kept refrigerated at 41°F (5°C) or kept frozen. **Safety:** ● Maintain adequate refrigeration during the entire shelf-life. ● Discard if damaged, slimy, or shows signs of swelling to prevent *Clostridium botulinum*.	When using the cook-chill or Sous Vide method, TCS food must be cooled to 5°C (41°F) in the sealed package or bag, and: **Time/Temperature:** ● Cooled to 34°F (1°C) in sealed package within 48 hours and held at that temperature for no more than 30 days. ● Held at 41°F (5°C) or less for no more than 7 days. **Safety:** ● The stored food must be consumed or discarded within 30 days from its date of packaging.

UHT and Aseptically Packaged Food

Pasteurized (UHT) food is placed into sterilized packaging (Aseptically Packaged) within a sterilized environment to prevent the entry of microorganisms.

Time:

● Varies: adhere to the use-by date

Temperature:

● Unopened: room temperature

● Opened: TCS food refrigerated at 41°F (5°C)

Safety:

● Discard if damaged

Summary

The theme of this chapter is to understand how food is to be safely stored until needed within a food operation. This involves describing the types of storage and their associated temperatures. It also includes knowing what requires date marking and how to rotate food, so the older products are used first. When a food manager trains and monitors staff on these essential topics, the operation will minimize lost revenue due to wasted food and avoid disastrous foodborne illness outbreaks.

Remember these food storage basics:

- Store RTE foods separately from raw foods to prevent cross-contamination
- Separate fish, raw meat, and poultry
- Keep food in clean containers or wrappers
- Keep storage areas, dollies, and food-transporting carts clean and dry
- Never store trash or soiled equipment in a food storage space
- Keep all chemicals in their original labeled containers
- Store chemicals away from food
- Store food at least 6 inches off of the floor

The Student's Workbook

As assigned by your instructor, use the separate Student's Workbook to work independently or in groups. Activities for this week's chapter include:

- Create a refrigerator storage plan poster
- Vote on the best (and completely accurate) poster in the class
- Watch the video and reflect
- Discuss the risks of each ingredient in the steak & baked potato recipe
- Make a list of equipment needed
- Produce the recipe
- Review the cleaning and sanitizing checklist
- End of chapter review video

Review Questions

Use these questions to check your knowledge of the material in this chapter. Your instructor has the answers.

1 The temperature for refrigerated storage is

a. 45°F (7°C) or below

b. 41°F (5°C) or below

c. 0°F (-18°C) or below

d. 50°F – 70°F (10°C – 21°C)

2 Which food must be stored below all others listed

a. Poultry

b. RTE food

c. Ground meat

d. Seafood

3 In storage, food must be stored

a. 4" above the floor

b. 5" above the floor

c. 6" above the floor

d. 1 foot above the floor

4 Whole potatoes should be stored in

a. Window sill

b. Walk-in cooler

c. Dry storage

d. Walk-in freezer

5 When moisture in the air becomes liquified, it is called

a. Condensate

b. Water

c. An accident

d. Comminuted

6 When contaminated food is made safe to eat, it has been

a. Re-purposed

b. Sanitized

c. Adulterated

d. Reconditioned

7 Ready-to-eat TCS foods can be stored in refrigeration for

a. 7 days minimum

b. 24 hours

c. 7 days maximum

d. 5 days maximum

8 The purpose of the FIFO method?

a. Rotate product

b. Keep staff busy

c. Tidy shelves

d. Reduce dust buildup

Chapter 8

Food Preparation

Introduction

Consuming cooked food is one of the main reasons people go out to eat. This chapter covers the important aspects of food preparation. As always, a recurring theme will be that of food safety and preventing foodborne illness, to keep the consumer safe and coming back for more!

The preparation process often begins with the need to thaw food. The process of thawing food is important and should never be done at room temperature (even at home) as too much time is spent in the temperature danger zone and bacteria can quickly multiply to unsafe levels.

The next step involves cooking the food to the proper minimum internal temperature, for a minimum amount of time, to inactivate pathogens. The combination of time and temperature varies based on the type of food and if it has been processed. There are also special restrictions related to serving raw or undercooked food when requested by a consumer.

If the cooked food is not meant for immediate service or is intentionally partially cooked, there are specific post-cooking requirements to keep the food safe for later consumption. This includes quickly cooling and then, later, quickly reheating the food to minimize the time spent in the temperature danger zone.

Key Terms

Keep an eye out for these essential topics:

- Additives
- Slacking
- Pooled eggs
- Variance

- Regulatory authority
- Minimum internal temperature
- Partial cooking
- Customer Advisories

Objectives

After working through this chapter, you should be able to explain the following to friends and family:

- Understand how to safely thaw TCS foods
- Learn about working with fresh produce
- Describe the minimum internal cooking temperatures
- Understand the importance of consumer advisories
- Describe the proper cooling requirements
- Explain the restrictions for highly susceptible populations

Monica, *Executive Vice President*

Monica enjoyed a great career so far in the foodservice industry. It was over a decade since she completed high school, with certifications from her culinary arts class. Her next move was to an exemplary accredited technical college to hone her skills. She started working for a casual dining chicken restaurant here in the pretty southern city.

She started as a general utility assistant, where most of her duties included cleaning. After two months and some unforeseen staff turnover, she had the most seniority for her position. She felt down, several of her friends had taken other jobs, and she was thinking of looking elsewhere. Shortly before the end of her shift, Demarius, her manager, called her into his office. "Oh boy," she thought, "am I in trouble?"

Demarius was a straight talker, right to the point with every conversation. "You are awesome," he said as she took a seat. He had noticed that she not only did her job well, she took the time to help the new employees get up to speed in their roles. She had patience, empathy, and insistence on precision with everything she did and taught. This was the springboard moment Monica needed. In the years following, with the help of great mentors at school and work, she graduated college and climbed the corporate ladder. She now holds the position of Executive Vice President for corporate food safety and earns a six-figure salary. She teaches the employees with patience, empathy, and precision. She has one big number she teaches more than any other… **Keep everyone alive, cook the chicken to 165!**

References in this Coursebook:

Glossary reference: Orange text means the definition of the word can be found in the Glossary located in the Student Workbook.

Food Code section reference: To verify or further study topics covered in this Coursebook, the FDA Food Code section numbers are provided in the margins. The current version of the offical code may be download here: https://www.fda.gov/food/retail-food-protection/fda-food-code

Preparation

Food preparation involves processing, seasoning, cooking, and/or combining products and ingredients from approved and reputable sources. The prepared food is available for immediate service or stored for later use. This activity within the kitchen includes many safety protocols that must be followed to ensure the prepared food is safe for consumption. Food safety controls include achieving minimum internal temperatures, monitoring the time food spends in the temperature danger zone, and post-cook storage requirements.

Safe Food Handling Review

Food managers must ensure staff follow safe food practices and take immediate corrective action when necessary. Many of the safe food handling practices that pertain to food preparation have been covered in previous chapters, for example:

Handling Food Safely

- Practice good personal hygiene
- Personal eating and drinking restrictions
- Wash hands properly
- Wear protective coverings
- Report personal health issues

Food Hazards and Allergens

- Bacterial, physical, and chemical hazards
- Foodborne illness — The big 6
  - Prevent cross-contamination
  - Use clean food contact surfaces
  - Use color-coded cutting boards
- Allergens — The big 9
  - Prevent cross-contact
  - Cook and temperature do not inactivate
  - Use color-coded cutting boards and utensils
- Intentional contamination
  - Prevent with a food defense program

TCS Foods and Controls

- Time/Temperature for Safety Foods (TCS Foods)
  - Raw animal food
  - Raw seed sprouts
  - Cut leafy greens, cut tomatoes, cut melon
  - Garlic-in-oil
  - Heat-treated animal or plant food (i.e., cooked or pasteurized)

- Monitor time and temperature
  - Use a calibrated thermometer
  - Use the correct thermometer
  - Ensure final cook temperature

Storage

- Remove only portions required for preparation
- Immediately return unused portions to refrigeration
- Follow date marking rules
  - Mark if not used within 24 hours
  - Discard if not used within (7) days
  - Combined ingredients must use the earliest date
- Ensure proper separation when returning unused food to storage
  - Space horizontally

  - RTE and cooked foods
  - Seafood, eggs
  - Intact meats
  - Non-intact meats
  - Ground meats
  - Poultry

Annex 7, Page 33

Preventing food contamination is a high priority for health inspectors. The following are two related examples in the Food Code where an inspector must mark the food establishment as "out" of compliance during an inspection.

- "When a multi-use piece of equipment such as a slicer or can opener is visibly soiled and being used at the time of the inspection. This item is also marked OUT if it is observed that equipment or utensils that have come into contact with a major food allergen such as fish was not cleaned and sanitized prior to use for other types of raw animal foods."

- "This item is marked OUT of compliance if food is found unsafe, adulterated, not honestly presented, from an unapproved source, or if ready-to-eat food is contaminated by employees and is not discarded or reconditioned according to an approved procedure, or if previously served unwrapped, unprotected food is observed being re-served."

See chapter 14 for more information on inspections and the consequences of Food Code violations.

Additives

3-202.12
3-302.14
3-601.12(B)

Food **additives** are sometimes used to preserve, season, or change the color of food. Additives must be approved and used within regulated amounts. A critical concept to understand is maintaining honesty in the foods presented for consumption and the potential for chemical contamination when additives are abused.

Food additive guidelines:

- Restrictions do not apply to food additives that are considered Generally Recognized as Safe (GRAS), such as salt, pepper, etc.
- A manager must be able to explain how additives found on the premises are used.
- Even approved additives must only be used as authorized by law.
- Color additive examples:
  - Allowed: Adding color to a red velvet cake.
  - Illegal: Adding red coloring to ground beef that has oxidized.
- Sulfites
  - Used to preserve food and retard discoloration associated with spoilage.
  - Must never be applied to fresh produce intended for raw consumption.

Consumers can have adverse reactions when sulfites are used indiscriminately to retard the natural browning of fruits and vegetables or make meat look brighter red.

Thawing

Time/Temperature for Safety (TCS) foods must be appropriately thawed to limit the potential for surviving bacteria to grow to unsafe levels and/or produce toxins. Suppose TCS food thawing occurs due to time/temperature abuse and is refrozen. In that case, the significant bacterial payload and/or preformed toxins are preserved and become a ticking timebomb during subsequent preparation. The main thawing goal is to limit the time a TCS food spends in the temperature danger zone.

3-501.13

Requirements

Time/Temperature for Safety (TCS) foods must be thawed as follows:

Thawing method	Notes
Refrigeration	Food is thawed in a refrigerator or walk-in cooler. ● Thawing food never exceeds 41°F (5°C) and therefore does not enter the temperature danger zone. ● The time required to thaw food varies based on food size/density.
Running water	Food is thawed while wholly submerged under running water. ● Water must be drinkable (potable) ● Sink, equipment, and utensils must be clean and sanitary ● Required water temperature: 70°F (21°C) or below ● Adequate water pressure to displace and drain off loose particles ● No portion of a thawing TCS food may rise above 41°F (5°C) for more than 4 hours, which includes: **Water exposure time + cook prep time = 4 hours max**
Cooking	Food is cooked from a frozen state. ● Food must be cooked to the required internal cooking temperature for the specific food item.
Microwave	Food is thawed in a microwave from a frozen state. ● Final cooking must commence immediately, with no interruption in the process ● Final cooking must be done in conventional cooking equipment, such as an oven or fryer
ROP fish	Reduced oxygen packaging (ROP) fish labeled "keep frozen until time of use" shall be removed from the reduced oxygen environment: ● Before using the refrigeration thawing method ● Before or immediately after using the running water thawing method

Once TCS foods are thawed, the storage requirements apply, such as time limits and date marking.

Annex 3, Page 113

From the FDA Food Code:

As an added safeguard to prevent the possibility of C. botulinum toxin formation, the Food Code requires that any frozen ROP fish that does not have barriers to the growth of C. botulinum in addition to refrigeration be completely removed from the ROP environment or package prior to thawing. This is to discourage the practice of thawing frozen ROP fish and holding it at 41°F (5°C) or less for a prolonged time period and/or selling it as a refrigerated product.

Slacking Method

3-501.12

Some food products, especially those intended for deep-fat frying, are often slacked (not thawed) before cooking. The process involves partially thawing food which is subsequently cooked to ensure a consistent heat penetration. Some jurisdictions allow slacking at room temperature, but a system must be in place to ensure the food never exceeds 41°F (5°C).

According to the Food Code, food that is slacked to moderate the temperature shall be held:

● Under refrigeration that maintains the food temperature at 41°F (5°C) or less; or

● At any temperature if the food remains frozen.

KEY TERM

Slacking The process of moderating the temperature of a food such as allowing a food to gradually increase from a temperature of -10°F (-23°C) to 25°F (-4°C) in preparation for deep-fat frying or to facilitate even heat penetration during the cooking of previously block-frozen food such as shrimp.

TCS Foods

Time/temperature for safety (TCS) foods have specific details which must be considered during the preparation process.

Figure 1

TCS food preparation Basics:

3-401

- **Required portions:** Only pull required portions from cooler/frozen storage
- **Large batches:** Break a large project down into small, manageable batches
- **Keep separate:** prevent cross-contamination and cross-contact
- **Clean and sanitize:** food contact surfaces, equipment, and utensils, between uses
- **Prompt storage:** Unused portions must be promptly refrigerated or frozen
- **Date-marking:** Apply date-marking if not consumed within 24 hours of preparation
- **Monitor time and temperature:** Avoid time-temperature abuse

Additionally, consider these food-specific guidelines:

Meat, Poultry, and Seafood

To prevent cross-contamination, remember to separate raw animal foods and use clean and sanitized utensils, food contact surfaces, and cutting boards.

Ready-to-eat (RTE) or fully cooked meat, poultry, or seafood must be handled with utensils or single-use gloves and never with bare hands.

Deli Salads

Deli salads are salads that contain TCS foods. Examples of deli salads include ham salad, chicken salad, egg salad, seafood salad, pasta salad, potato salad, and macaroni salad.

Figure 2

When prepared in the food operation, this combination product must be carefully managed for time/temperature abuse to avoid the growth of *Listeria monocytogenes*, for example.

Suppose a seafood salad is a featured menu item, and a large batch must be made ahead of time. The food handler should only remove enough product from refrigerated storage as needed to prepare manageable portions to prevent time/temperature abuse of ingredients. No cooked or refrigerated component should be outside of refrigeration for more than 4 hours.

Before preparation, chilling ingredients, such as canned or jarred items, will help maintain a lower temperature outside of refrigeration. Consider using shallow storage pans to help the product cool more quickly once date-marked and placed in refrigeration.

Annex 5, Page 24

FDA Food Code Instructions to Inspectors:

Special attention should be given to the potential for hands as a vehicle of contamination. Ensuring that hands are washed using the proper procedure and at the appropriate times must be a top priority during every inspection. Data show that viruses can be tenacious even in the presence of good handwashing. Inspectors should observe employee use of utensils and gloves during the preparation and service of ready-to-eat foods and ingredients, such as salads and sandwiches.

Shell Eggs and Egg Products

Eggs and egg products have several requirements as a TCS food and a Big 9 allergen.

Egg definitions:

Annex 3, Page 3

- *Avian species only:* Chicken, duck, goose, guinea, quail, ratites, or turkey.
- **Shell eggs:** Raw eggs still in their shell. Typically not pasteurized.
- **Hard-boiled egg:** Fully cooked shell egg, with shell intact.
- **Egg products:** Eggs removed from their shell and processed (with or without additional ingredients), pasteurized, and packaged.
- **Pooled eggs:** Combining two or more eggs, removed from their shell, into a container.

Pooled eggs

Eggs should be pooled just before cooking/baking or promptly stored at 41°F (5°C) or below. If allowed to stand for any length of time, pathogens from one egg can contaminate the batch.

Figure 3

Highly susceptible population

The Food Code restricts the use of eggs or egg products when serving a highly susceptible population (HSP), such as a school with young children or a senior living center. This does not apply to an individual customer in a food establishment.

3-501.19(D)

Pasteurized eggs or egg products *must be substituted* for raw eggs in the preparation of:

3-801.11

- Foods such as Caesar salad, hollandaise or Béarnaise sauce, mayonnaise, meringue, eggnog, ice cream, and egg-fortified beverages.

  -- and --

- Recipes in which eggs are pooled, with the following *exceptions*:
  - Single serving: Shell eggs added just before cooking a single serving for immediate service
  - Baking: Shell eggs combined as an ingredient just before baking

Hard-boiled eggs

Hard-boiled eggs may or may not be a TCS food depending on how they are cooled after cooking.

Annex 3, Page 114

- **Air-cooled:** Not a TCS food
- **Water cooled:** Is a TCS food

The potable water that comes into contact with the egg may contain pathogens that may pass through the egg shell while cooling.

Batters and Breading

When preparing a batter from scratch or breading food, it is crucial to prevent cross-contamination and avoid time-temperature abuse.

Definitions:

Batter: A semi-solid flour-based food mixed with other ingredients such as liquids (e.g., milk, eggs, oil), sugar, and/or leavening. Examples include cakes, pancakes, and pastries.
Examples: onion rings, shrimp, vegetables, Korean-style fried chicken

Breading: Used as a coating for baked or fried food, which usually consists of three separately applied layers: Flour (dry), an egg mixture (wet), and a dry mixture of dried bread or cracker crumbs often mixed with seasonings.
Examples: chicken parmesan, fish, southern-style fried chicken

In the three-step breading process, once the flour has been contaminated with the egg dip, it must be treated as a TCS food and stored or disposed of accordingly.

Figure 4

Plant Foods (Fruits & Vegetables)

Since they are ready-to-eat (RTE) at any temperature, plant foods do not require the same initial pathogen control as do raw animal foods. When cooked, they only need to reach the temperature required for hot holding (covered in the next chapter) of 135°F (57°C); bacterial growth is generally prevented at this temperature. One exception, starting with the 2022 Food Code, is commercially packaged foods not processed to control pathogens or if cooking instructions are provided, are not considered ready-to-eat.

3-401.13

3-401.15

Washing

Most fresh produce must be washed thoroughly to remove contaminants as much as possible. However, according to the FDA, some bacteria develop a biofilm that reduces the ability to wash bacteria off, even with antimicrobial agents.

Possible fresh produce contaminants:

- Chemicals – e.g., pesticides
- Pathogens – e.g., salmonella spp., Hepatitis A, E. coli

Unless commercially washed, precut, and bagged, all fresh produce must be thoroughly washed under running, potable water before eating, cutting, or cooking (chemical washing allowed if properly tested). Additionally, it is crucial to remove soil and debris before peeling or altering the produce's form to prevent cross-contamination.

3-302.15
Annex 3, Page 93

Produce washing guidelines:

- Do not wash precut or prewashed bagged produce
- Wash sink before and after
- Properly wash hands
- Avoid soap, detergent, or other surfactants
- Wash water should be 10°F (-12°C) warmer than the produce being washed
- Avoid soaking or submerging
- Watch for stem scars, cracks, cuts, or bruises
- Brush scrubbing only on produce with tough rind or peel (e.g., carrots, cucumbers, citrus fruits)
- Dry with a clean cloth towel or fresh disposable towel

TCS Foods

After being cut, leafy greens, melons, and tomatoes are considered TCS foods and, therefore, should avoid time/temperature abuse by storing in refrigeration at 41°F (5°C) or lower.

Highly Susceptible Populations

The FDA and CDC have issued health advisories that HSP persons should avoid eating raw alfalfa sprouts (aka raw seed sprouts) until intervention methods are in place to improve the safety of these products.

Ice

Seemingly harmless, ice must be carefully considered by a food manager since it is consumed (making it food) or comes into contact with food.

Ice as a food

3-202.16

When used as a food or cooling medium, ice must be made from potable water; i.e., deemed drinkable according to the EPA. This requirement stems from the fact that freezing water does not prevent bacteria's destruction and may preserve it.

Ice as a cooling medium

3-303.11

Ice used as a cooling medium, e.g., cooling canned beverages or melons, must subsequently never be used as a food or food ingredient. The ice is considered contaminated and could lead to foodborne illness if consumed.

3-203.11(C)
3-303.12

Packages held in ice should be inspected for water tightness or damage to prevent melted ice water from entering and contaminating the contents. Additionally, although potentially separated at first, contamination may occur as ice melts, and water drains onto adjacent foods. This can result in cross-contamination (pathogens) and/or cross-contact (allergens).

Figure 5

Ice Scoops

3-304.12(E)

When ice is made or stored in a bin, a scoop must be used (see photo) to gather it, and never bare hands. When not in use, ice scoops must be stored:

- In a clean, protected location

  -- or --

- In a container of water maintained at 135°F (57°C) that is cleaned frequently

4-204.13

Alternatively, an operation may choose to use an overhead ice dispenser, which precludes staff or consumers from contaminating stored ice.

Figure 6

Fresh Juice

Specific rules apply when fresh juice is packaged in a food establishment as opposed to being sourced from a commercial processing facility.

3-202.110

Juice Packaged On-Site

Juice packaged in a food establishment for sale shall be:

3-404.11

- **Treated**: under an HACCP plan (covered in chapter 13) to achieve a 99.999% microorganism reduction

  -- or --

- **Labeled**: juices not treated must bear the following warning:

> "WARNING: This product has not been pasteurized and, therefore, may contain harmful bacteria that can cause serious illness in children, the elderly, and persons with weakened immune systems."

> **KEY TERM**
>
> **Juice** A liquid, purée, or concentrate extracted from the edible portions of one or more fruits or vegetables. For purposes of HACCP, juice does not include liquids, purées, or concentrates not used as beverages or ingredients of beverages.

Highly Susceptible Populations

When considering fresh juice restrictions, the FDA Food Code expands the definition of young children from "preschool age children" (i.e., children under age 5) to children age 9 or less.

3-801.11

The following criteria apply to juice:

- Prepackaged juice or a prepackaged beverage containing juice labeled as not specifically processed to prevent, reduce, or eliminate the presence of pathogens may not be served or offered for sale.

- Unpackaged juice prepared on the premises must be processed according to an HACCP plan (HACCP plans are covered in chapter 13).

Variances

8-103

A variance allows a food operation to do something otherwise not permitted by the **regulatory authority** or Food Code. If the variance request is a multi-state or inter-state commerce issue, the FDA determines (i.e., allows or denies) at the federal level. Otherwise, the state, local, or tribal regulatory authority determines unless they are technically unable, in which case they can refer the request to the FDA. A condition of an approved variance often requires an HACCP plan that accounts for potential food safety risks associated with the intended preparation process.

> **KEY TERM**
>
> **Variance** A written document issued by the regulatory authority authorizing a modification or waiver of one or more requirements of the FDA Food Code if, in the opinion of the regulatory authority, a health hazard or nuisance will not result from the modification or waiver.

Variance examples:

- Smoking raw animal food as a preservative rather than a flavor enhancement
- Shellstock display tanks used to store or display living molluscan shellfish intended for human consumption
- A food does not require time/temperature control for safety

Cooking

3-401

Pathogens that cause foodborne illness are killed or reduced to safe levels when cooked to the required **minimum internal temperature** as specified in the FDA Food Code. There are several factors used to determine the required temperature. This includes food bulk/size, post-cooking heat rise, and pathogen numbers and varieties; the latter is why poultry requires more cooking and shell eggs less.

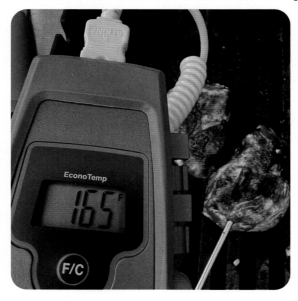

Cook temperatures must be checked with a clean, sanitized, and calibrated thermometer for the minimum required time. Doing so will ensure food is safe for consumption.

Figure 7

Best Practices

Cooking food in a busy kitchen involves managing several important aspects simultaneously. The following list is a helpful reminder of best practices related to cooking.

Cooking best practices:

Preparation

- **Personal** hygiene: Ensure hands are washed and protective coverings are used as needed
- **Required portions:** Only pull required amounts from cooler/frozen storage
- **Thawing:** As described previously in this chapter; never at room temperature
- **Clean and sanitized:** Food contact surfaces, equipment, and utensils, between uses
- **Keep separate:** Prevent cross-contamination and cross-contact

Cooking

- **Monitor time and temperature:** Achieve proper temperature to destroy pathogens effectively
- **Raw or undercooked:** Minimum surface temperature and color change on all sides
- **Microwave:** Cover to retain surface moisture and rotate/stir for even heating
- **Partial Cooking:** Used to save time later, must be properly cooled and cooked later

Storage

- **Prompt storage:** Avoid time-temperature abuse for TCS foods
- **Date-marking:** TCS foods require date-marking if not consumed within 24 hours of preparation

---

KEY TERM

Intact Meat means a cut of whole muscle(s) meat that has not undergone comminution, mechanical tenderization, vacuum tumbling with solutions, reconstruction, cubing, or pounding (aka non-intact meat).

Time and Temperature

The following table summarizes the **minimum internal cooking temperature** and **minimum required cooking time** as dictated by the Food Code.

Food Item	Minimum internal cook temperature	Minimum required cook time
Plant foods (if cooked) • Vegetables, fruit, grains	135°F (57°C)	Instantaneous
Raw animal foods • Fish (Seafood) • Intact Meat: cuts and steaks of beef, pork, veal, and lamb • Commercially raised game animal, rabbits **Shell Eggs (Raw)** • Cooked for immediate service	145°F (63°C)	15 seconds
Non-Intact Meat Comminuted raw animal foods: • Ground meat • Ground fish Mechanically tenderized meats *Disrupting muscle fibers with needles or blades* • Intact meat: cuts and steaks of beef, pork, veal, and lamb Injected meats: *Internally marinated with juices, broth, spices* • Briskets, brined ham **Ratites:** *Mostly flightless birds with long necks and legs* • Ostrich, Rhea, and Emu **Shell Eggs** • Not cooked for immediate service	155°F (68°C) *Alternatively:* 145°F (63°C) 150°F (66°C) 158°F (70°C)	17 seconds 3 minutes 1 minute Instantaneous
Poultry • Whole or ground chicken, duck, or turkey **Wild** game animal – i.e, not commercially raised **Stuffed** fish, meat, pasta, poultry, or ratites **Stuffing containing** fish, meat, poultry, or ratites	165°F (73°C)	< 1 second (instantaneous)
Whole meat roasts • Beef, corned beef, lamb, pork, cured pork	*See table in next section*	
Tea	175°F (79°C)	Instantaneous

3-401.13

3-401.11(A)(1)

3-401.11(A)(2)

3-401.11(A)(3)

3-401.11(B)

Game animal includes mammals such as reindeer, elk, deer, antelope, water buffalo, bison, rabbit, squirrel, opossum, raccoon, nutria, or muskrat, and nonaquatic reptiles such as land snakes. It does not include ratites, or livestock such as horses, sheep, or goats.

Roasts

When cooking a roast, the Food Code allows multiple combinations of time and temperature to accommodate various cooking methods and desired results. Each temperature/time combination has the same effect of killing bacteria in the roast. To help explain this, consider the following hypothetical situation:

3-401.11(B)

Imagine the bacteria is a lobster in a pot of water. This is how the crustation feels when the water temperature is:

- 70°F (21°C) — *A day at the beach.*
- 100°F (38°C) — *Do I have a fever?*
- 120°F (49°C) — *That's a hot day in Death Valley!*
- 130°F (54°C) — *Death is inevitable.*

Although the temperature is not as high as those listed in the previous table, the bacteria eventually become overwhelmed when cooked for an extended period.

There are time-temperature combinations that do not work. With a high oven temperature, a roast may heat too quickly and cause the outside to dry or char. An insulating layer is created, which prevents the heat from penetrating all parts of the food properly. Conversely, cook times of greater than 6 hours in the 50°F - 130°F (10°C – 54°C) range are particularly hazardous given the potential for excessive bacterial growth.

Time and Temperature

The following table summarizes the minimum internal cooking temperature and minimum required cooking time, specifically for roasts, as dictated by the Food Code. As the temperatures rise, the listed time changes from minutes to seconds.

Whole Meat Roast	Temp.	Time (Minutes)	Temp.	Time (Seconds)
• Beef, corned beef, lamb, pork, and cured pork roasts such as ham	130°F (54°C)	112	147°F (64°C)	134
	131°F (55°C)	89	149°F (65°C)	85
	133°F (56°C)	56	151°F (66°C)	54
	135°F (57°C)	36		
• Heat all parts of the food	136°F (58°C)	28	153°F (67°C)	34
to a temperature for	138°F (59°C)	18	155°F (68°C)	22
the holding time corre-	140°F (60°C)	12		
sponding to that tem-	142°F (61°C)	8	157°F (69°C)	14
perature, as shown here.	144°F (62°C)	5	157°F (70°C)	0
	145°F (63°C)	4		

Oven Types and Temperatures

3-401.11(B)(2)

When cooking a roast, the Food Code provides the following oven type/temp table to achieve the required temperature in the specified amount of time, based on the roast size.

Oven type	Less than 10 pounds (4.5 kg):	10 pounds (44.5 kg) or more:
Still dry	350°F (177°C) or more	250°F (121°C) or more
Convection	325°F (163°C) or more	250°F (121°C) or more
High humidity	250°F (121°C) or less (Roasts of any weight)	

Raw or Undercooked

In some cases, based on a consumer's specific order, raw or undercooked animal food may be served. The following list is related guidelines from the Food Code.

3-401.11(C)

Whole-muscle, intact beef

Raw or undercooked, allowed if:

- Not serving a highly susceptible population (HSP)
- "Whole-muscle, intact beef" as defined below
- The top and bottom are cooked to a surface temperature of 145°F (63°C)
- A cooked color change is achieved on all surfaces

3-401.11(D)

Egg, fish, marinated fish, molluscan shellfish, steak tartare,

partially cooked food, lightly cooked fish, soft cooked eggs,

rare meat other than whole-muscle, intact beef steaks

Raw or undercooked, allowed if:

- Not serving a highly susceptible population (HSP)
- Selections offered on a children's menu do not contain comminuted meat
- Proper consumer advisory is given (covered later in this chapter)
- A variance has been granted

It is never permitted to serve raw or undercooked animal food cooked using the non-continuous (aka paracook) process

The non-continuous (aka paracook) process is covered later in this chapter.

KEY TERM

Whole-muscle, intact beef means whole muscle beef that is not injected, mechanically tenderized, reconstructed, or scored and marinated, from which beef steaks may be cut.

Food commonly served raw or undercooked:

Raw or Undercooked Animal Food (proteins)	Menu Items
Beef	Steak tartare, hamburgers, carpaccio, seared mechanically tenderized steak
Poultry	Roasted duck breast (legs are tougher and generally slow cooked)
Eggs	Soft-cooked eggs (soft boiled, poached, sunny side up, over-easy); Eggs used as an ingredient (Caesar salad, hollandaise, beverages, aioli, tiramisu, mousse, meringue pie, puddings, or custards)
Fish	Sushi, raw-marinated fish, cold smoked fish, ceviche, tuna carpaccio, seared tuna, gravlax, crudo
Shellfish	Oysters, clams, mussels

Microwave Cooking

Given the rapid increase in temperature while cooking food in a microwave oven, the same level of bacterial destruction is not achieved. Therefore, food cooked in a microwave oven must reach an internal temperature of 165°F (73°C) in all parts of the food.

3-401.12

Guidelines for cooking raw animal foods in a microwave:

- Throughout/midway through cooking, rotate and/or stir (heat distribution)
- Cook covered to retain surface moisture
- Heated to a temperature of 165°F (73°C) in all parts (pathogen destruction)
- Check the internal temperature in multiple locations
- Cover and let food stand for (2) minutes (thermal equalization)

To avoid cross-contamination, microwave ovens should be cleaned and sanitized, inside and out.

Partial Cooking

3-401.14

In support of a busy kitchen or large event, **partial cooking** (a.k.a., paracooking or non-continuous cooking) is employed - which includes a partial initial cook, cooled quickly, and then a final cook. This multi-step process allows some work to be completed ahead of time but still offers the consumer the freshness and quality of a final cook. However, due to the complex cook method, where the food goes through the temperature danger zone multiple times, a food safety manager must take steps to avoid foodborne illness.

Examples of when partial cooking is used:

- Grill-marking chicken breasts for a large-scale off-site catering event
- Mass production of steaks and/or chicken breasts for a large private party
- Partially cooked hamburger patties held for final preparation and service during rush hour

Requirements for raw animal foods using the partial cook method:

- Initial cook does not exceed (60) minutes.
- Immediate cooling as required for TCS foods (covered later in this chapter)
- Hold frozen or refrigerated as required for TCS foods (covered in the previous chapter)
  - ○ With label and date-marking
  - ○ Refrigeration: 41°F (5°C) or below
- Final cook to the required minimum internal temperature
- Serve immediately,

  or

- Hot hold at the minimum required temperature (covered in the next chapter), *or*
- With approval, variance, or a proper plan, store food as required for TCS foods

Safety Requirements

Consumer Advisories

3-603

A consumer advisory lets customers know that food served in a raw or undercooked state may be more likely to cause foodborne illness. This advisory must be written and posted conspicuously where the consumer can see it, such as in the menu or a table tent. When menus are updated, the food manager must consider whether any new foods require a consumer advisory.

Customer advisories are required when the following raw or undercooked animal foods are served:

- Raw oysters
- Food containing a sulfiting agent
- Wild mushrooms
- Raw or unpasteurized milk (variance required from DHEC)
- Unpasteurized juices
- Raw seed sprouts offered for immediate consumption

Customer advisories require a disclosure and a reminder.

Disclosure

A disclosure clearly identifies the raw or undercooked animal food by using words like "raw" or "undercooked" in the written description of the food. Alternatively, an asterisk may be placed next to the food description, along with a footnote indicating the food is served raw or undercooked.

Reminder

A reminder states that eating raw or undercooked food increases the risk of foodborne illness. The reminder must include an asterisk by the menu item and a footnote.

Examples

In the following consumer advisory examples, the disclosure is in **bold**, and the reminder is in *italics*:

Oysters on the half shell **(raw oysters)***	Oysters on the half shell*	Two eggs*served with grits and toast
Hamburger **(cooked to order)***	Hamburger*	Hamburger*
Ceviche **(raw fish)***	Ceviche*	Ceviche **(raw fish)***
Consuming raw or undercooked meats, poultry, seafood, shellfish, or eggs may increase your risk of foodborne illness	***These items are served raw or undercooked, or contain, or may contain, raw or undercooked ingredients.** *Regarding the safety of these items, written information is available upon request.*	**Eggs and hamburger may be served raw or undercooked.** *Consuming raw or undercooked meats, poultry, seafood, shellfish, or eggs may increase your risk of foodborne illness, especially if you have a certain medical condition.*

Highly Susceptible Populations

3-801

Most people who experience foodborne illness have mild symptoms, may miss work time, and are not part of a recognized outbreak. However, for some within our population, a foodborne illness can be more serious, even life-threatening. The level of severity cannot be predetermined for an individual, but a specific population has been identified as most susceptible, which includes:

- Preschool age children
- Older adults in health care facilities
- Those with impaired immune systems

The Food Code describes this group as a **highly susceptible population** (HSP) and includes the following food preparation restrictions:

The following ready-to-eat foods may not be served or sold:

- Raw animal foods such as raw fish, raw-marinated fish, raw molluscan shellfish, and steak tartare,
- A partially cooked animal food such as lightly cooked fish, rare meat, soft-cooked eggs that are made from raw eggs, and meringue; *and*
- Raw seed sprouts (e.g., raw alfalfa sprouts)
- Fresh juice restrictions listed previously in this chapter

Children's Menus

3-401.11(D)(2)

The Food Code prohibits offering specific high-risk TCS foods like burgers, eggs, and shellfish as raw or undercooked on children's menus. Therefore, these menu items do not require a consumer advisory.

Figure 8

Post-Cooking

Once food has been cooked, it is served immediately, or additional prescriptive steps are taken to ensure it remains safe to consume. This last section focuses on the primary post-cooking steps, including cooling, freezing, and reheating.

Cooling

When cooked food is refrigerated and stored for later use, it must first be cooled quickly to limit time spent in the temperature danger zone and thus limit the potential for bacterial growth.

3-501.14

- Temperature danger zone: 41°F – 135°F (5°C – 57°C).
- Bacterial growth maximized: 70°F – 125°F (21°C – 52°C)

Within 6 hours, cooked food must be cooled:

- From 135°F (57°C) to 70°F (21°C) within 2 hours, *and*
- To 41°F (5°C) or below within 6 hours total

Notice that during the first two hours, the cooling food is in the most dangerous range of the temperature danger zone. When food is not cooled per the Food Code requirement, pathogens may grow to hazardous levels and lead to foodborne illness.

The 2-hour and 6-hour times are both maximum time limits. It is permissible, for example, to cool food to 70°F (21°C) in just 1 hour and complete the entire process in 4 hours. The time required to cool food varies based on the size and density of each food item. Refrigerated storage is designed to keep cold foods cold, not to cool foods quickly. Therefore, several requirements and methods exist to cool food safely.

Requirements

The Food Code outlines the following requirements for proper and safe cooling.

Cooked TCS foods must be cooled:

- Within 2 hours, from 135°F (57°C) to 70°F (21°C);

  and

- Within a total of 6 hours, from 135°F (57°C) to 41°F (5°C) or less.

For ambient temperature ingredients, such as canned tuna, TCS foods must be cooled:

- Within 4 hours, to 41°F (5°C) or less.

Whole turkeys, roasts, and large tightly sealed containers take more time to dissipate the heat and cool down than loosely covered shallow containers or smaller separated food items. Therefore, a food manager should have a plan that modifies production (passive, smaller batches) or uses alternative cooling methods (active, specialized tools and equipment).

Alternative methods to traditional cooling include using an ice paddle or a blast chiller. These highly effective options include low temperatures and high circulation to reduce food temperature quickly and limit bacterial growth.

According to the Food Code, cooling shall be accomplished by:

- Placing the food in shallow pans
- Separating the food into smaller or thinner portions
- Using rapid cooling equipment
  - Ice paddle or blast chiller
- Stirring the food in a container placed in an ice water bath
- Using containers that facilitate heat transfer
- Adding ice as an ingredient, *or*
- Other effective methods

When placed in cooling or cold-holding equipment, food containers in which food is being cooled shall be:

- Arranged within the equipment to provide maximum heat transfer through the container walls,

  and

- Loosely covered or uncovered if protected from overhead contamination during the cooling period to facilitate heat transfer from the surface of the food

Although most options are listed, the Code is vague enough, e.g. "use rapid cooling equipment" or "other effective methods," to allow for new and creative alternatives.

Methods

3-501.15

The following are standard methods and tips used to cool food properly.

Shallow pan method

Use shallow metal pans 2" to 4" (5 cm – 10 cm) deep to reduce product thickness.

- Optimal: pre-chill pans
- Refrigerate immediately
- Loosely cover and don't stack hot pans to improve circulation
- Cut or slice whole/ thicker animal food into portions no larger than 4" (10 cm)

Figure 9

Ice bath method

The ice bath method uses both ice and water. The food does not come into direct contact with the ice or water. However, clean potable water must be used for the ice and water.

- In a clean and sanitized sink or large pan, fill it with ice and then cold water
- Divide product into 1 gallon or smaller containers
- Immerse smaller containers in the larger ice bath until the product is level with ice/water
- Use a spoon, ice paddle, or similar mixing device to stir and agitate every 10 minutes
- As the ice melts, drain the water and replenish the ice
- Monitor the temperature of food using a clean and sanitized thermometer
- Refrigerate immediately after the food has cooled to 41°F (5°C)

Figure 10

Ice as an ingredient

Ice may be added directly to the product as an ingredient. As the product cools, the water from the melted ice combines with the food. Consideration must be given to the final texture and taste of the food when using this method. The ice must be made from potable water and not have been used previously as a cooling medium (i.e., ice bath).

3-202.16

Blast chiller

Use rapid chill refrigeration equipment that facilitates quick cooling food.

Food cooling tips:

- Never allow foods to cool at room temperature
- Plastic is an insulator, so never cool foods in plastic containers
- Test your cooling process to ensure it works, then document it
- Use a log to ensure required times and temperatures are achieved
- Discard food that does not cool properly

Health Department Inspection

Annex 7, Page 36

The food safety manager should understand what an inspector is looking for as it relates to properly cooling food. Consider the following summarization from the Food Code:

FDA Food Code

Because the entire cooling process is difficult to observe during an inspection, the inspector may ask the person in charge (PIC) if any foods are currently cooling when they first arrive. If so, temperatures are taken to determine if proper cooling is possible with the procedures being used. Discussions with the PIC along with observations are used to determine compliance. For instance, during the discussion, the PIC says that a food product was cooled overnight in the walk-in cooler. The product is checked, and the temperature is 50°F (10°C). Eight hours have elapsed from closing to opening. This item will be marked "out of compliance" because the product did not cool from 135°F to 70°F (57°C to 21°C) within two hours, and from 135°F to 41°F (57°C to 5°C) or less within a total of 6 hours.

Reheating

3-403

Once food has been properly cooked, cooled, refrigerated -- or frozen and properly thawed -- it might finally be reheated prior to service. Food is either reheated for immediate service or hot holding.

For Immediate Service

Fully cooked and refrigerated food may be served at any temperature when prepared for immediate service in response to a consumer's order. For example, a roast beef sandwich with au jus may be reheated or served cold. Remember this is a ready-to-eat (RTE) food, so bare hand contact is prohibited.

For Hot Holding

When food is reheated and not intended for immediate service, the Food Code requires food to pass through the temperature danger zone quickly.

Using a conventional oven to reheat food previously prepared in-house:

- Reheat from 41°F to 165°F (5°C to 74°C) within 2 hours
- Hold at 165°F (74°C) for 15 seconds

Using a microwave oven to reheat food previously prepared in-house:

- Reheat from 41°F to 165°F (5°C to 74°C) within 2 hours
- After reheating, stir product and cover. Leave covered for 2 minutes

Using a conventional or microwave oven to reheat processed food, opened, and reheated:

- Reheat from 41°F (5°C) or ambient temperature to 135°F (57°C) within 2 hours

Reheating food tips:

- Never use hot holding equipment to reheat food (see next chapter)
- Do not mix new or fresh food with leftover items
- Stir foods frequently to distribute the heat
- Measure the internal temperature with a clean thermometer
- After reaching the required temperature, the food must be held at 135˚F (57°C) or above as covered in the next chapter

Corrective Action

When TCS foods are not reheated to 165°F (74°C) in 2 hours, the food must be discarded. No further reconditioning is allowed.

Food Donation

Food waste is estimated to be 30 - 40 percent of the supply created. To support people in need and to avoid wasting energy used to grow, process, and transport food and excessive landfill material, the FDA encourages donating unused food.

Annex 3, 3-204.10

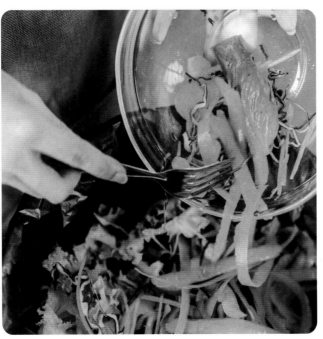

Figure 11

Food stored, prepared, packaged, displayed, and labeled in accordance to law and the Food Code may be offered for donation.

3-204.10

Conversely, food not otherwise fit to be served in a food establishment may not be donated. including contaminated or timer/temperature abused food.

The purpose of the Food Code is to safeguard public health and ensure that food is safe, unadulterated, and honestly presented when offered to the consumer or donated.

8-101.10

Summary

The theme of this chapter is to understand how food is thawed, cooked, cooled, and later reheated safely. Highly susceptible populations must be given special consideration as prescribed in the Food Code, especially when serving raw or undercooked animal food.

Although there are a lot of temperatures listed in this chapter, many of them relate closely to the temperature danger zone. The following is a simplification of the temperatures and times covered.

Temperature danger zone:

- Temperature danger zone: 41°F – 135°F (5°C – 57°C).
- Bacterial growth maximized: 70°F – 125°F (21°C – 52°C)

Thawing highlights:

- Never thaw at room temperature
- No portion of a thawing TCS food may rise above 41°F (5°C) for more than 4 hours
- Microwave thawing must be followed by immediate cooking

Cooking highlights:

- Plant foods   135°F (57°C)   Instant.
- Seafood, steak   145°F (63°C)   15 sec.
- Burgers, large birds 155°F (68°C)   17 sec.
- Poultry, wild game   165°F (73°C)   Instant.

Cooling highlights:

- From 135°F to 70°F (57°C to 21°C) within 2 hours, *and*
- To 41°F (5°C) or below within 6 hours total

Reheating highlights:

- Reheat from 41°F to 165°F (5°C to 74°C) within 2 hours
- Hold at 165°F (74°C) for 15 seconds

The Student's Workbook

As assigned by your instructor, use the separate Student's Workbook to work independently or in groups.

Activities for this week's chapter include:

- Create a "bread petri dish"
- "Is it safe?" game
- Watch the video and reflect
- Discuss the risks of each ingredient in the tomato sauce recipe
- Make a list of equipment needed
- Produce the recipe
- Review the cleaning and sanitizing checklist
- Fill out the recipe and cost form
- End of chapter review video

Review Questions

Use these questions to check your knowledge of the material in this chapter. Your instructor has the answers.

1 Which is not an approved thawing method:

a. Under running water

b. Room temperature

c. Refrigeration

d. Microwave oven

2 Which is not a shell egg according to the Food Code:

a. Alligator

b. Duck

c. Chicken

d. Turkey

3 When cooked, plant foods should be cooked to:

a. 155°F (68°C)

b. 145°F (63°C)

c. 135°F (57°C)

d. 165°F (73°C)

4 Raw poultry should be cooked to:

a. 155°F (68°C)

b. 145°F (63°C)

c. 135°F (57°C)

d. 165°F (73°C)

5 A roast cooks at an internal temperature of 130°F (54°C) for?

a. 112 minutes

b. 120 minutes

c. 28 minutes

d. 4 minutes

6 A consumer advisory must include:

a. Disclosure

b. Time and temperature

c. Disclosure and reminder

d. Reminder

7 Food must cool to 70°F (21°C) within

a. 6 hours

b. 24 hours

c. 2 hours

d. 4 hours

8 Food must be reheated from 41°F to 165°F (5°C to 74°C) within

a. 6 hours

b. 24 hours

c. 2 hours

d. 4 hours

Chapter 9

Food Service

Introduction

Once the food is properly cooked, reheated, or cooled (as covered in the previous chapter) it may be held for service until needed. Time/temperature for safety (TCS) food must be properly managed to prevent bacterial growth that can lead to foodborne illness.

Presenting food to a consumer is the last step in the flow of food. At this point the servers have specific requirements to prevent food and beverage contamination just before and while the consumer has the food in their possession. Food employees must carefully monitor self-service areas such as buffets and salad bars as well.

Finally, most of these Food Code requirements apply to off-site activities such as catered events or temporary food establishments. In fact, there are additional rules designed to keep food safe while being transported or served in an outdoor environment.

Key Terms

Keep an eye out for these essential topics:

- Hot & cold holding for service
- Time as a Public Health Control
- Tableware
- Multi-use to-go containers
- Catering
- Mobile units
- Temporary food establishments
- Vending machines

Objectives

After working through this chapter, you should be able to explain the following to friends and family:

- Understand the reason for hot and cold holding requirements
- Learn about holding without temperature control
- Explore the requirements for setting a table
- Understand the safety protocols for self-service areas
- Learn about the off-site operations and requirements
- Explain the safety requirements for vending machines

Aliyjah,
Assistant Food & Beverage Manager

It's a new week and a new challenge, thought Aliyjah. She always had a positive outlook on life, especially after her health scares a few years ago. Life taught her that she needed to go and look for the good things and victories and this was a new week and a new opportunity.

She has three new front of the house employees starting this week, as the restaurant is getting busier and the staff they have are getting stretched pretty thin. As the Assistant Food & Beverage Manager, she is the supervisor in charge of front of the house training. Her responsibilities also filtered down to maintaining general service, too, but training had become a bigger focus recently, with the restaurant's struggle to maintain a high quality staff. As she planned out in her mind about all the things her new team mates would achieve today, she planned the agenda. First things first, they would learn about food safety. This is something that many restaurants address once they have a problem with the health inspector or an illness occurs—when it comes to the front of house. For Aliyjah the safety of the food from the grower to the kitchen and to her customers was key to their success.

She would listen to a talk radio show each week who described the dirtiest restaurants on health inspections and all the terrible mistakes they would make. Often the infractions would be on time and temperature abuse issues, cross-contamination and on service mistakes, like handling ready to eat foods with bare hands. I don't ever want to be on the news, if it's for that reason, she thought to herself as she walked in the door to the three smiling new recruits.

"Good morning everyone, let's get started!"

Holding Food

Once time/temperature control for safety (TCS) food has been adequately cooked, reheated, or cooled, it is either served immediately or held and monitored to avoid time/temperature abuse. Bacterial growth is optimal when TCS food is in the temperature danger zone, so the Food Code has specific requirements the food safety manager must adhere to when holding food for service. Food that falls outside the parameters of this section must be discarded to avoid foodborne illness, which also has a financial impact on the food operation.

There are three scenarios for holding food — hot, cold, and without temperature control. Each will be covered in this section, but first, here are the highlights.

- Temperature danger zone: 41°F – 135°F (5°C – 57°C).
- Bacterial growth maximized: 70°F – 125°F (21°C – 52°C)

When holding time/temperature control for safety (TCS) food, it shall be maintained:

Hot Holding for Service

At 135°F (57°C) or above

Exception: Properly cooked roasts, 130°F (54°C) or above

3-501.16(A)(1)

Cold Holding for Service

At 41°F (5°C) or below

3-501.16(A)(2)

Holding without Temperature

- Hot food starting at 135°F (57°C) or above, up to 4 hours.
- Cold food starting at 41°F (5°C) or below,
  - Up to 4 hours (no temperature monitoring)
  - Up to 6 hours if it *never rises above* 70°F (21°C).

3-501.19

COLD HOLDING

HOT HOLDING

Figure 1

1.1

Hot Holding for Service

Figure 2

Once a TCS food has been adequately cooked or reheated, if not immediately served, it must be held at a minimum temperature (or higher) to remain safe for consumption. This is called **hot holding for service**.

According to the CDC, food held at improper temperatures has led to approximately 250,000 foodborne illnesses attributed to *C. perfringens* and *B. cereus* each year in the United States. Therefore, maintaining adequate hot holding temperatures is a critical public health intervention to inhibit bacterial growth. Given the current scientific understanding, including some margin of error for temperature fluctuations, the FDA deems maintaining hot TCS food at a temperature of 135°F (57°C) is sufficient to prevent bacterial growth and, therefore, an effective measure in the prevention of foodborne illness.

3-501.16(A)(1)

Highlight	Maintain hot food at 135°F (57°C) or above Exception: Properly cooked roasts may be held at 130°F (54°C) or above
Why	Bacterial growth can occur in food if it is held at a temperature within the temperature danger zone, which is between 41°F − 135°F (5°C − 57°C)
Who	Food managers and their food employees are responsible for hot holding
When	Hot holding temperature/time control for safety (TCS) food for display or service
Where	All hot holding units used for service, hot holding, display, and transport, such as: • Service line • Soup pots • Display line • Hot holding cabinets • Steam tables
How	Proper holding temperatures must be maintained during display, storage, and transportation. Consider the following best practices: • Check food temperatures regularly, and take corrective action as necessary • Use the proper equipment for hot holding • Stir the product frequently to distribute the temperature • Covered foods maintain temperature

Cold Holding for Service

Once a TCS food has been adequately cooked and cooled, or after opening a commercially processed food package, if not immediately served, it must be held at a maximum temperature (or lower) to remain safe for consumption.

Cold holding can simply mean a food item is stored in a walk-in cooler (see chapter 7 for cold storage details). More specifically, **cold holding for service** means the food is actively kept cold in the kitchen (e.g., use as an ingredient), in self-service (e.g., consumer accessed buffet), in a public display, or transit to an off-site location (e.g., a catering event).

Pathogenetic growth is limited when TCS foods are maintained under the cold temperature control requirements of the FDA Food Code. This includes time control and other intrinsic and extrinsic factors defined by FAT TOM, as covered in chapter 3. The main goal is to prevent foodborne illness from consuming contaminated food and minimize loss of revenue due to the disposal of food due to mismanagement.

Highlight	Maintain cold food at 41°F (5°C) or below Frozen food must remain frozen	3-501.16(A)(2)
Why	Bacterial growth can occur in food if it is held at a temperature within the temperature danger zone, which is between 41°F – 135°F (5°C – 57°C)	
Who	Food managers and their food employees are responsible for cold holding	
When	Cold holding temperature/time control for safety (TCS) food for display or service	
Where	All cold holding units used for service, hot holding, display, and transport, such as: • Salad bars • Display line • Cold holding cabinets • Walk-in coolers • Commercial refrigerators	
How	Proper holding temperatures must be maintained during display, storage, and transportation. Consider the following best practices: • Check food temperatures regularly, and take corrective action as necessary • Do not mix old food with fresh batches of food • Use the proper equipment for cold holding • Place prepared food into the cold holding unit as soon as possible • Do not overload cold holding unit • Ensure indicating thermometers are correctly placed and working properly in cold holding units	

Figure 3

Time as a Public Health Control (TPHC)

3-501.19

Based on everything previously covered in this section, it is understandable that holding ready-to-eat TCS foods without temperature control has significant public health implications and must be properly controlled. In this scenario, time is the primary mechanism used to prevent foodborne illness.

 Hot Food

Hot food starting at 135°F (57°C) or above may be held up to 4 hours after it is removed from temperature control.

 Cold Food

Cold food starting at 41°F (5°C) or below can be held up to 4 hours after it is removed from temperature control if the temperature is not monitored.

Cold food starting at 41°F (5°C) or below can be held up to 6 hours after it is removed from temperature control if the temperature is monitored and *never rises above* 70°F (21°C).

 Ambient Temperature Food

Ready-to-eat plant food (fruits or vegetables) or hermetically sealed food starting at 70°F (21°C) or below, that becomes a TCS food when cut or opened, can be held up to 4 hours as long as it never exceeds 70°F (21°C).

Ready-to-eat TCS food held without temperature control must never be returned to temperature control, and any remaining portions must be discarded after the time limit has lapsed.

Once a food begins to warm to room temperature after being removed from refrigeration, the primary pathogen of concern is *Listeria monocytogenes*. However, cold TCS foods held without temperature control can reach any temperature as long as they are consumed or discarded within four hours.

Figure 4

Time as a public health control (TPHC) might be used to display ready-to-eat TCS food for sale (see photo), or ingredients (working supply) held on hand while cooking for immediate service.

Specific examples include:

- Cut leafy greens or tomatoes on a buffet
- Milk at a barista station
- Shell eggs on a cookline
- Waffle batter at a self-serve continental breakfast area
- During a power outage

TPHC Restrictions:

- TPHC is not allowed in some jurisdictions
- Food may not be returned to temperature control
- Written procedures shall be prepared in advance
- Raw eggs may not be made available, for self-service, to highly susceptible populations

Date-marking is a critical TPHC step to ensure food is consumed in a specific timeframe or discarded. Therefore, TPHC food must be marked to indicate when the item must be discarded. Additionally, food found in unmarked containers or packages must also be discarded.

Serving Food

In a food establishment, properly prepared food is ready to be served to the consumer by servers or waitstaff. This last step in the flow of food includes some additional safeguards in the Food Code to prevent contamination. This includes how tables are set, how plates and cups are handled, and certain self-service requirements.

In addition to all the methods listed in this section to prevent contamination, the Food Code provides a blanket statement that food must be protected from contamination by a factor or source not specified in the Food Code.

Tableware

Managers must train and monitor staff to ensure tableware, e.g., plates and cups, is stored and handled correctly to prevent contamination. Corrective action should be taken when violations are observed, which includes retraining, replacing tableware, or replacing food or a beverage.

> **KEY TERMS**
>
> **Tableware** means eating, drinking, and serving utensils for table use such as flatware including forks, knives, and spoons; hollowware including bowls, cups, serving dishes, and tumblers; and plates.
>
> **Utensil** means a food-contact implement or container used in the storage, preparation, transportation, dispensing, sale, or service of food, such as kitchenware or tableware that is multiuse, single-service, or single-use; gloves used in contact with food; temperature sensing probes of food temperature measuring devices; and probe-type price or identification tags used in contact with food.
>
> **Single-service articles** means tableware, carry-out utensils, and other items such as bags, containers, placemats, stirrers, straws, toothpicks, and wrappers that are designed and constructed for one time, one person use after which they are intended for discard.

4-904.11

Food Code requirements for handling tableware:

- Staff must not touch parts of tableware that come into contact with food or lips
- Unwrapped knives, forks, and spoons must be presented by their handles
- At self-service areas, consumers may only touch the handles of utensils
- Single-service items must remain in the original wrapper or be dispensed from an approved dispenser accessed by the consumer

3-304.14(A)

Wiping Food Spills:

A server's cloth, used for wiping food spills from tableware, must be maintained dry and not used for any other purpose.

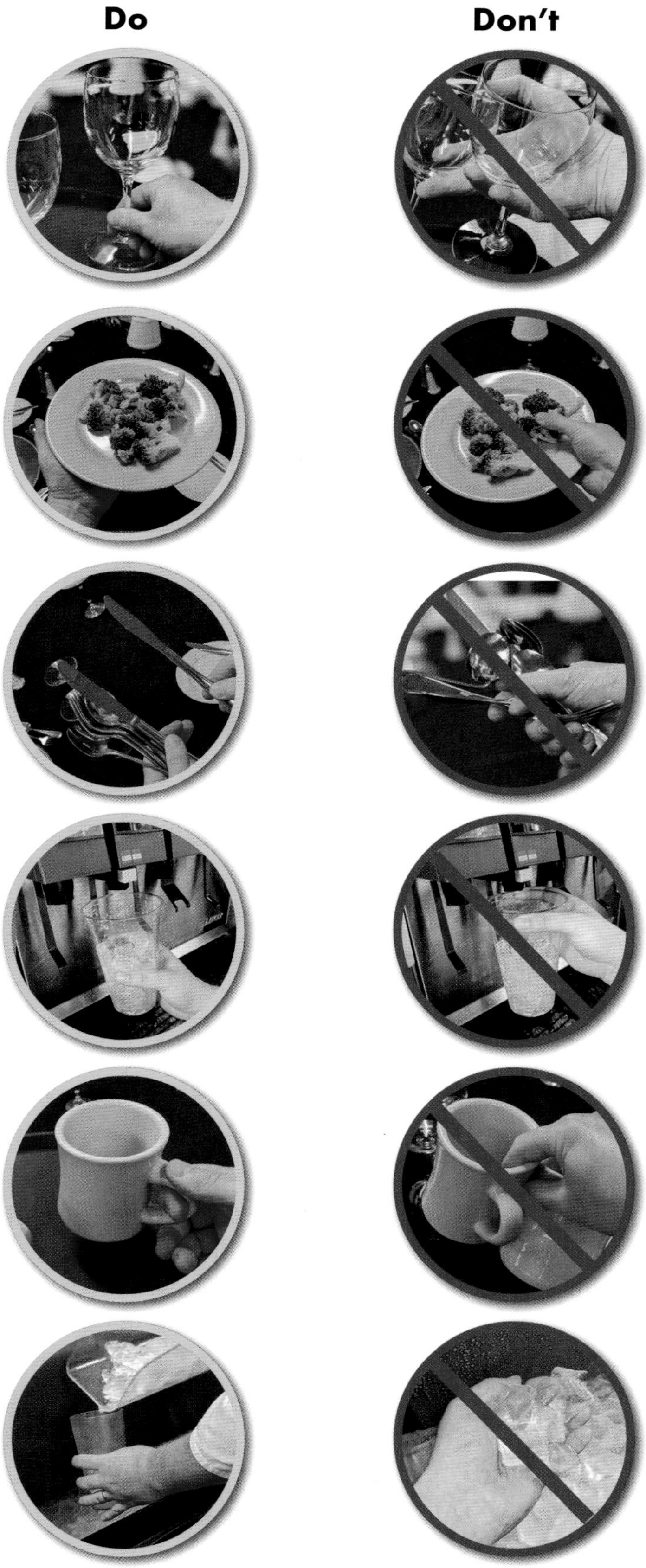

Figure 5

Preset Tableware

4-904.13

Some food operations will choose to preset tables with plates, cups, and flatware to save time or for aesthetic appearance. The Food Code has requirements related to preset tableware to prevent contamination of food and lip-contact surfaces. It also covers when unused tableware may be reused if a table is not seated to its total capacity.

Figure 6

Food Code requirements for **preset** tableware:

- Wrapped, covered, or inverted

  -- or --

- Allowed to be exposed, if

  ○ Unused settings removed when table is seated

    -- or --

  ○ Unused settings are cleaned and sanitized before reuse

These requirements are why we often see coffee cups or wine glasses turned upside down when seated at a table in a food establishment. The staff knows to remove entire place settings at empty seats, but they may not know if the consumer will have a particular type of beverage. Once they take the drink order, they will remove any unnecessary cups or glasses. Although accessible by the consumer for a time, cleaning and sanitization are not required before another consumer reuses.

Refills, Returns, and Re-Service

Once food is served to a customer, restrictions exist on when (or if) it may be offered to another consumer.

Food Code requirements for **returned** or **re-service** of food:

- Consumer returned or unused food may not be reused
- Exception: non-TCS food may be reused, *if:*
  - Container closed between uses, such as ketchup, steak sauce, or wine bottle
  - Unopened original package in sound condition, such as crackers, salt, or pepper

Servers must use clean and sanitized tableware when providing second portions or **refills**. The only exception is refilling beverages so long as there is no contact between the pouring utensil and the lip-contact area of the cup.

If a food operation allows **multi-use to-go containers**, such as a thermal non-spill coffee cup, to be reused, the food employee must visually inspect it to verify it has been cleaned. Obviously soiled items should be rejected to prevent cross-contamination of equipment, such as a beverage dispenser.

3-306-14

Self-Service Areas

Figure 7

Self-service areas such as buffets, salad bars, sushi bars, or display cases require specific controls to prevent accidental or intentional contamination. Staff must be properly trained to monitor these areas and take corrective action if necessary. For example, staff should know that customers are not allowed to reuse plates when returning to a buffet, but may reuse a cup to refill a beverage.

3-306

3-304.16

Self-service requirements:

Food

- Monitor time and temperature for RTE/TCS foods
- Stir foods frequently to distribute the temperature
- Never mix new food with old food
- Cover containers when not in use
- Raw animal foods are not allowed, except:
  - ○ Sushi or raw shellfish
  - ○ Ready-to-cook portions, e.g., Mongolian style BBQ (see photo)
  - ○ Raw or frozen shell-on lobster or shrimp

Figure 8

Equipment and Utensils

- Sneeze guards installed
- Dispensers must be cleaned prior to restocking
- Utensils should be provided for each food item and replaced when soiled
- Knives, forks, and spoons must be stored in a way that the consumer grabs the handle
- Single-use utensils must be in their original wrapper or dispensed from an approved device

Signs and Labels

2-103.11(M) & 3.304.16

- Label each food item
- A sign must be posted requiring a clean plate for second portions (see photo)
- A consumer advisory sign is required when offering allowed raw animal foods

> **Please use a clean plate each time you visit the food bar.**
>
> **Thank you!**

Figure 9

Off-Site Service

The FDA Food Code applies to all off-site operations as the definition of a food establishment which includes a restaurant, delivery (i.e., bulk transportation), catering, temporary venues, mobile units, and vending machines. Check with your local jurisdiction for specific rules and permit requirements.

2-301.12

> **KEY TERM**
>
> **Food Establishment** means an operation that:
>
> - Stores, prepares, packages, serves, vends food directly to the consumer, or otherwise provides food for human consumption such as a restaurant; satellite or catered feeding location; catering operation if the operation provides food directly to a consumer or to a conveyance used to transport people; market; vending location; conveyance used to transport people; institution; or food bank; *and*
> - Relinquishes possession of food to a consumer directly, or indirectly through a delivery service such as home delivery of grocery orders or restaurant takeout orders, or delivery service that is provided by common carriers.
>
> **Off-site service means** catering and vending activities located away from where the food was originally prepared and cooked.

Transportation

When food is prepared at a primary food operation and then transported (i.e., delivered) to an off-site location for service, care must be taken to adhere to all Food Code requirements for time and temperature control for TCS foods.

Annex 3, 8-203.10, #3
Annex 5, Page 20

Food must be properly packaged and stored to prevent cross-contamination. The delivery vehicle is the storage space, and all related Food Code storage requirements apply — such as product labeling, date-marking, temperature control, and separation.

Immediate corrective action must be taken for any time/temperature abuse or cross-contamination discovered.

The person in charge (PIC) must also ensure any delivery person not employed by the food operation complies with the Food Code while in the food operation and in possession of the food.

Catering

For the context of this section, a catered event is a one-time event such as a wedding reception or a business conference located away from the primary food operation. The number of people served can range from just a few to over ten thousand. The location can also vary and be hosted at places like a golf club, a community center, an office, a conference center, a religious facility, or in a field. The off-site location may have commercial-grade food service equipment and potable water, or it may not even have power.

Given all these variables, the food manager must ask the right questions and spend quality time preparing for a successful and safe off-site catering event since the same Food Code rules apply. The event must meet the Food Code off-site safe operation requirements, including water supply, sewage disposal, and utilities.

5-103.12

Figure 10

Menu and food flow determine the equipment required for food storage and holding for service. Space must be established for waste and dirty dishes and located away from food storage, preparation, and service areas. Additionally, food must be protected from insects, pests, dust, and other environmental contaminants during storage, preparation, transportation, and serving. A robust food defense program must be in place to avoid intentional contamination.

Avoid these catering pitfalls:

- Poor employee health and hygiene
- Food from unsafe sources
- Improper cooking temperatures and times
- Inappropriate hot and cold-holding equipment, temperatures, and times
- Cross-contamination, cross-contact, and contaminated equipment

Temporary Food Establishment

A **temporary food establishment** provides food to consumers for a limited time, whether the food is paid for or not. This service is often during an event, such as a fair, festival, celebration, or cultural program. The Food Code applies to temporary food establishments and even includes specific requirements.

Figure 11

KEY TERM

Temporary food establishment means a food establishment that operates for a period of no more than 14 consecutive days in conjunction with a single event or celebration.

Food Code-related requirements:

- **Floors** may be concrete or asphalt if sloped to a drain, e.g., a parking lot.
  - ○ Alternatively, dirt/gravel if covered with mats to control dust and mud
- **Walls** and **ceilings** may be constructed of a material that protects the interior from the weather and windblown dust and debris.
- Handwashing sinks necessary, providing one minimum, for convenient use by employees.
- Adequate (permanent or temporary) water supply, sewage disposal, and utilities.

6-101.11(B)

6-201.18

Figure 12

Mobile Units

Annex 7, Page 61

The definition of a mobile unit can vary from pushcarts to full food preparation vehicles. The Food Code defines **mobile units** as food operations unless it only offers prepackaged foods that are not time/ temperature control for safety (TCS) foods.

Figure 13

Mobile units may be subject to all Food Code provisions that apply to food establishments. Consult the local regulatory authority for specific local requirements. They may require auxiliary support services such as a commissary or **servicing area** based on the menu, type of operation, and availability of onboard or on-site equipment.

> **KEY TERM**
>
> **Servicing area** means an operating "base location" to which a mobile food establishment or transportation vehicle regularly returns for such things as vehicle and equipment cleaning, discharging wastes, refilling water tanks and ice bins, and boarding food.

Vending Machines

There are several safety requirements for **vending machines** since the **vending machine location** is often unattended.

> **KEY TERM**
>
> **Vending machine** means a self-service device that, upon insertion of a coin, paper currency, token, card, or key, or by electronic transaction or optional manual operation, dispenses unit servings of food in bulk or in packages without the necessity of replenishing the device between each vending operation.
>
> **Vending machine location** means the room, enclosure, space, or area where one or more vending machines are installed and operated and includes the storage areas and areas on the premises that are used to service and maintain the vending machines.

Figure 14

Vending machine requirements:

- TCS food must be in its original packing
- Condiments must be in individual packages or an approved dispenser
- The dispensing compartment shall be protected with a cover or self-closing door to prevent contamination and tampering when located outside or unattended
- Cutting or piercing parts of can openers shall be protected from manual contact, dust, insects, rodents, and other contamination
- For TCS food options, an automatic shutoff must prevent dispensing if the following requirements are not met:

  ○ In a refrigerated vending machine, the ambient air temperature may not exceed 41°F (5°C) for more than 30 minutes immediately after the machine is filled, serviced, or restocked;

  or

  ○ In a hot holding vending machine, the ambient air temperature may not be less than 135 °F (57 °C) for more than 120 minutes immediately after the machine is filled, serviced, or restocked.

Annex 3, 4-204.14

4-204.19

4-204.111

Summary

The theme of this chapter is to understand how food makes it from the kitchen to the consumer. Sometimes it happens immediately, but other times it may need to be delivered or held for service until needed. The hot and cold holding requirements are meant to prevent bacterial growth and keep food safe.

When food is served away from the primary food establishment, most of the Food Code is applicable. In fact, there are additional requirements to keep food safe from the less controlled surroundings.

Temperature danger zone:

- Temperature danger zone: 41°F – 135°F (5°C – 57°C).
- Bacterial growth maximized: 70°F – 125°F (21°C – 52°C)

Hot holding for service:

- Maintain hot food at 135°F (57°C) or above
- Exception: Properly cooked roasts may be held at 130°F (54°C) or above

Cold holding for service:

- Maintain cold food at 41°F (5°C) or below
- Frozen food must remain frozen

Time as a Public Health Control (TPHC):

Hot food held without temperature control

- Hot food starting at 135°F (57°C) or above may be held up to **4 hours** after it is removed from temperature control.

Cold food held without temperature control

- Cold food starting at 41°F (5°C) or below can be held up to **4 hours** after it is removed from temperature control if the temperature is not monitored.
- Cold food starting at 41°F (5°C) or below can be held up to **6 hours** after it is removed from temperature control if the temperature is monitored and never rises above 70°F (21°C).

The Student's Workbook

As assigned by your instructor, use the separate Student's Workbook to work independently or in groups.

Activities for this week's chapter include:

- Measure & record temperature reductions for sauces
- Watch the video and reflect
- Discuss the risks of each ingredient in the Bechamel sauce recipe
- Make a list of equipment needed
- Produce the recipe
- Review the cleaning and sanitizing checklist
- Fill out the recipe and cost form
- End of chapter review video

Review Questions

Use these questions to check your knowledge of the material in this chapter. Your instructor has the answers.

1 Hot food may be held without temperature control for up to:

a. 2 hours

b. 4 hours

c. 6 hours

d. No limit

2 Cold food may be held without temperature control for up to:

a. 2 hours, if temp never rises above 70°F (21°C)

b. 4 hours, if temp never rises above 70°F (21°C)

c. 6 hours, if temp never rises above 70°F (21°C)

d. No limit, if temp never rises above 70°F (21°C)

3 Properly cooked roasts may be held at:

a. 130°F (54°C)

b. 155°F (68°C)

c. 135°F (57°C)

d. 165°F (73°C)

4 Hot food may be held with temperature control for:

a. 2 hours

b. 4 hours

c. 6 hours

d. No limit

5 When refilling a cup, never touch

a. The lip contact area

b. The bottom

c. The middle

d. No such restriction

6 How may forks, knives, and spoons be handled:

a. Not at all

b. Food contact area

c. Handles

d. Using a tissue

7 Which is not always considered a food operation:

a. Temporary units

b. Catering events

c. Mobile units

d. There are no exceptions

8 Vending machines dispensing TCS foods must:

a. Be bolted to the floor

b. Provide sanitizing wipes

c. Have an auto-shutoff feature

d. Have a can opener

Chapter 10

Cleaning & Sanitizing

Cleaning and sanitizing are essential and required steps in a food establishment. A properly cleaned and sanitized food-contact surface or piece of equipment is free of foreign particles and microorganisms, which could otherwise cause foodborne illness if consumed.

Cleaning and sanitizing are not the same thing. Cleaning removes the foreign particles, and sanitizing removes the microorganisms.

Most cleaning and sanitizing are proactive tasks and should be performed according to staff training and a master cleaning schedule. Some cleaning is reactive, such as someone getting sick and experiencing a sudden vomiting or diarrheal event.

Key Terms

Keep an eye out for these essential topics:

- Cleaning
- Sanitizing
- Food-contact surface
- Concentration
- Personal protective equipment (PPE)

- Water hardness
- Chlorine
- Iodine
- Quaternary ammonium (Quats)

Objectives

After working through this chapter, you should be able to explain the following to friends and family:

- Understand the difference between cleaning and sanitizing
- Learn about hot water sanitizing & chemical sanitizing
- Explore the requirements for dishwashing
- Understand how to protect clean items from contamination
- Describe the seriousness of responding to a sudden sickness
- Explain the time limits associated with cleaning equipment and utensils

Harley,
Manager

Harley loves their job. It was not something they had planned when they went to the career days in high school, but it was a happy accident. About three years ago Harley graduated high school and didn't really have a definitive direction for their life. They enjoyed their science classes, especially chemistry. They also enjoyed their culinary arts class, too. After a short stint in a very busy restaurant as a server, they decided that not only were the late-night hours not for them, but the stress was not a positive thing in their life. While for some it is character-building, for them, a mad customer was just too much to handle after an eight-hour shift on their feet.

One day as they arrived to work the lunch shift, they bumped into a gentleman in a lab coat in the dish station. He was friendly and seemed to really know his trade. He worked for the chemicals company that provided all the cleaning supplies for the restaurant. It wasn't just a sales position though. He was calibrating the dishwasher too. He mentioned that they had an opening if Harley was interested, and they did all the training that was needed. After working out their notice at the restaurant, Harley started their training program and then shadowed other experienced employees. They were perfect for the job, as they had a dedication to service.

The knowledge they gained from the training was beneficial but joined with their passion for service and empathy for the restaurant owners, managers, and chefs with whom they worked made them a rock star in their eyes. It was not long before they started to manage a team and lead one of the most successful territories in the area. The businesses knew that they could rely on Harley and their team whenever they had a need and that they were always a priority.

As Harley looks back on the last few years, they love their job helping the hospitality industry do better. The best restaurants in the world can't operate without sanitation and safety at the top of their list.

Cleaning Equipment and Utensils

Cleaning and sanitizing are not the same thing. When tasked with cleaning and sanitizing equipment and utensils, it is vital to understand the following distinction:

- **Cleaning** is the process of removing visible organic matter and debris.
- **Sanitizing** is the process of destroying pathogenic microorganisms.
- An item must be cleaned before it can be properly sanitized.

This section covers cleaning, and the next section covers sanitizing.

Examples of items that require cleaning and sanitizing:

Equipment
- Deli meat slicer
- Mixer
- Oven

Food-Contact Surfaces
- Food preparation surface
- Cutting board
- Inside a microwave

Nonfood-Contact Surfaces
- Top of a microwave/shelving
- Walk-in walls/door
- Floors, Walls, Ceilings

Utensils
- Knives, spoons, tongs
- Can and bottle openers
- Ingredient measuring cups

Figure 1

KEY TERM

Food-contact surface means a surface of equipment or a utensil that food normally comes into contact with or an adjacent surface where that food may drain, drip, or splash.

Objective

4-601

A food-contact surface cannot be adequately sanitized until it is cleaned of organic matter. Cleaning nonfood-contact surfaces is also crucial in preventing the accumulation of pathogenic microorganisms and not attracting insects and pests.

Cleaning objectives:

- Equipment food-contact surfaces and utensils shall be clean to sight and touch.
- The food-contact surfaces of cooking equipment and pans shall be kept free of encrusted grease deposits and other soil accumulations.
- Nonfood-contact equipment surfaces shall be free of dust, dirt, food residue, and other debris.

Frequency

4-602

Cleaning is an essential step in preventing cross-contamination within a food establishment. Equipment and utensils used with TCS foods must be cleaned, at a minimum, every 4 hours.

When to clean:

- Before each use with a different type of raw animal food
- Switching tasks between raw foods and ready-to-eat foods
- Between uses with raw fruits and vegetables and with TCS foods
- Before using or storing a thermometer; *and*
- At any time during the operation when contamination may have occurred

There are exceptions to the last item, which allows working with a succession of raw animal foods requiring a higher cooking temperature, and similar products as long as cleaning occurs at least every **four hours**. Of course, while foods are deemed safe for consumption, the food manager must consider the possible effect on food quality and flavor influence when taking these exceptions.

Some equipment contacting non-TCS foods have less stringent cleaning requirements, such as:

- Iced tea dispensers and consumer self-service utensils such as tongs, scoops, or ladles shall be cleaned at least every 24 hours.
- Condiment dispensers and display containers shall be cleaned before restocking.
- Equipment shall be cleaned according to manufacturer instructions or, in the absence of manufacturer instructions, as necessary to prevent the accumulation of soil and mold.

Cooking and baking equipment, as well as the cavities and door seals of microwave ovens, must be cleaned at least every 24 hours.

Finally, anything else, i.e., nonfood contact surfaces, must be cleaned often enough to prevent the accumulation of soil residues.

> **KEY TERM**
>
> **Equipment** means an article that is used in the operation of a food establishment such as a freezer, grinder, hood, ice maker, meat block, mixer, oven, reach-in refrigerator, scale, sink, slicer, stove, table, temperature measuring device for ambient air, vending machine, or warewashing machine. It does not include hand trucks, forklifts, dollies, pallets, racks, and skids.

Methods

The Food Code outlines several methods for cleaning equipment and utensils based on equipment available, what needs to be cleaned, and the type of soil required to be removed.

4-603

Dry Cleaning

Dry Cleaning involves using dedicated equipment to brush, scrape, or vacuum food contact surfaces of dry food residue; TCS foods excluded.

Precleaning

Precleaning involves scraping equipment or utensils over a garbage disposal unit or trash can. The prewash cycle on a dishwashing machine also does this. When extremely soiled, pre-soaking or scrubbing with abrasives is sometimes required.

Washing (Wet Cleaning)

Washing involves removing or completely loosening soils using procedures based on the type of equipment or utensil and the type of soil to be removed. This may include manual or mechanical methods using detergents or emulsifiers--acid, alkaline, or abrasive cleaners (see types of cleaners below).

Rinsing Procedures

Rinsing Procedures involve rinsing with water or a detergent-sanitizer solution to remove cleaning chemicals. This is part of the 3-step washing procedure, which includes washing, rinsing, and sanitizing.

Cleaned in Place

4-603-15

Cleaned in Place is used when equipment is too large to fit in a sink or is fixed and cannot be moved. After unplugging from power, any removable parts shall be disassembled to enable adequate cleaning and sanitization. After allowing everything to air dry, they may be reassembled.

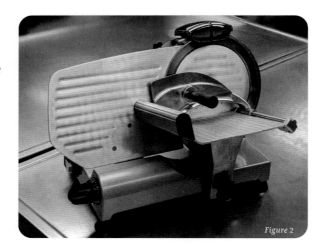

Figure 2

Types of Cleaners

4-603-14

This section briefly describes the types of detergents and soaps mentioned in the Food Code. Remember, the primary purpose of these products is to remove solid dirt and debris before sanitization. Follow the manufacturer's instructions to ensure safe use and avoid damaging or scratching incompatible surfaces.

Detergents (alkaline):

Detergents are alkaline cleaners that combine with and loosen debris and other impurities. They are a synthetic derivative of soap that dissolves more quickly in water.

Degreasers

A degreaser is a solvent-based cleaner that removes water-insoluble substances such as grease, oil, or lubricants. This cleaner is used on oven doors and other cooking areas to remove and prevent grease buildup.

Delimers (acidic)

Delimer is an acidic cleaner used to remove mineral deposits (lime and scale buildup) on surfaces and equipment affected by hard water deposits, such as dish machines and steam tables. This product must be used carefully and on the correct type of surface, per the manufacturer's directions, to avoid personal injury and surface damage.

Abrasive Cleaners

Abrasive cleaners contain small particles which help "scrub" at heavy dirt and stains. Caution should be used as some surfaces may be scratched when using abrasive cleaners.

Specialty Cleaners

Food operations often have many other specialty cleaners depending on foods and beverages prepared. For example, there are cleaners for deep fat fryer cleaners, beverage dispensers, micro-brewery equipment, etc. The distributor will often recommend products and provide training on how and when to use them.

Sanitizing Equipment and Utensils

As previously stated, cleaning and sanitizing are not the same thing. An item must be cleaned before it can be adequately sanitized. The previous section covered cleaning, and this section covers sanitizing.

> **KEY TERM** Sanitizing means the application of cumulative heat or chemicals on cleaned food-contact surfaces that, when evaluated for efficacy, is sufficient to yield a reduction of 5 logs, which is equal to a 99.999% reduction, of representative disease microorganisms of public health importance.

Cleaning and sanitizing cleaners can be dangerous to work with. Be sure to understand and follow all product and distributor instructions to keep staff and food safe. This includes any **personal protective equipment (PPE)** such as safety glasses, chemical-resistant gloves, and respiratory.

Objective

After cleaning correctly, pathogens may still be on wiping cloths, food equipment, or utensils. Therefore, sanitization is required to destroy these microorganisms of public health concern. It is essential that sanitization happen after proper cleaning and rinsing to achieve maximum benefit. For example, rinsing an item under potable water from the tap contaminates a previously sanitized thing.

4-701

Frequency

After cleaning and rinsing any food contact surface (covered in the previous section), sanitizing must be performed before it is used again.

4-702

Methods

Regardless of the method used, a manager must understand the surface contact **time** required for (hot water or chemical) sanitization to be effective at destroying pathogens. Additional factors include rinse pressure, temperature, and chemical concentration.

4-703

4-204-116
4-501-111

Hot Water

Hot Water sanitization (or heat sanitizing) is achieved when equipment or utensils are fully submerged for at least 30 seconds in 171°F (77°C) water. In-sink heating devices are often used to maintain the required water temperature.

Figure 3

Note: This temperature is close to the internal cook temperature for poultry. Both required temperatures have the goal of killing pathogens and preventing foodborne illness.

Chemical Sanitization

4-501-114

Chemical Sanitization involves the application of sanitizing chemicals by immersion, brushing, or pressure spray methods. The chemical shall only be used as intended, following instructions on an EPA-registered product label.

The minimum contact times to effectively destroy pathogens are listed in the following chart:

Solution	Chlorine		Iodine	Quats**
Minimum Temperature	100°F (38°C)	75°F (24°C)	68°F (20°C)	75°F (24°C)
Water hardness	*		*	500 ppm or less *
pH	10 or less	8 or less	5 or less*	*
Concentration	50-99 ppm	50-99 ppm	12.5 – 25 ppm	*
Minimum Contact time	7 seconds	7 seconds	30 second	30 seconds

* per manufacturer's EPA-registered label instructions for an effective solution
** Quats is short for quaternary ammonium

Solution Concentration

A cleaning solution **concentration** results from diluting a chemical cleaner with water following guidelines on the product label. For example, a specific cleaning product may call for 1 tsp of chlorine to every gallon of water to achieve a 65 ppm concentration.

Similar to how a combination of time and temperature are effective at destroying pathogens while cooking a roast, time and chemical concentration are essential to effective sanitization. A weaker concentration may not effectively destroy pathogens, while a stronger concentration may be unsafe to handle and even damage the surface being cleaned. Chemicals must always be diluted with water as specified on the product label and should never be used at full strength.

1 **Scrape and remove solid debris**

4-603.12

2 **Wash**

4-603.14

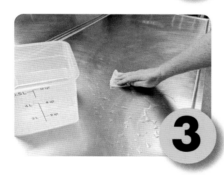

3 **Rinse**

4-603.16

4 **Sanitize**

4-703.11

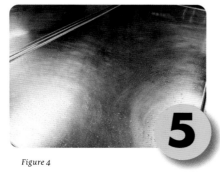

5 **Air dry**

4-901.11

Figure 4

Solution Test Kit

4-501-116

Since the effectiveness of chemical sanitizers is determined primarily by the concentration and pH of the sanitizer solution, testing is necessary to accurately determine the concentration of the chemical sanitizer solution. Test kits have strips that are dipped into a solution and then compared to a reference key based on the color change.

Figure 5

Water Hardness

4-501-114

When minerals are present in potable water it is considered hard water. Some organizations may use a water softening system to remove the minerals to avoid buildup on surfaces and extend the life of some equipment. The water hardness also affects sanitizers by reducing their effectiveness in some cases. The water hardness can be determined by testing or asking the local water authority. This information can then be used to determine the proper sanitizing product and concentration to use.

Warewashing

What is commonly called dishwashing, the Food Code refers to as warewashing, which includes food-contact surfaces of equipment. Warewashing is done using a dishwashing machine or manually, in a sink or in-place for non-movable equipment.

> **KEY TERM**
> **Warewashing** means the cleaning and sanitizing of utensils and food-contact surfaces of equipment.

Dishwashing Machine

Using a dishwashing machine involves placing pre-rinsed soiled cups and plates on racks which are then pulled through the required wash, rinse, and sanitize cycles (similar to some car washes) and allowed to air dry. This process can save staff time, and the machine uses hotter water or more potent chemicals resulting in a more consistent sanitization.

Figure 6

A dishwashing machine must have a visible data plate indicating the required conveyor speed, water temperature, and water pressure to ensure items are properly cleaned and sanitized. It must also have gauges to monitor water temperature/pressure and internal baffles to minimize internal cross-contamination. The unit needs to have a method of alerting the operator when the sanitizing chemicals should be refilled.

4-204.113

4-204.117

Dishwashing machine basics:

- Pre-rinse, scrape, or soak items to remove solid food particles
- Load racks correctly so all surfaces are sprayed and allowed to drain, avoid overloading
- Monitor the manufacturer's recommended wash and rinse temperatures and times
- Check final (sanitizing) rinse water pressure gauge
- Air-dry all items

Never rinse or towel dry items after they have gone through the dishwashing machine to avoid contamination. If any debris remains, the items must be scrubbed and re-washed.

Hot Water Sanitization Machines

Using high-temperature hot water in place of chemicals is an effective sanitization method. There is a maximum and a minimum temperature which must be monitored with a built-in thermometer. If the temperature is out of range, the unit must be serviced to avoid injury and ensure proper sanitization.

4-501-112

Dishwashing machine hot water temperatures requirements:

- 180°F (82°C) minimum water temperature
- 165°F (74°C) minimum water temperature for single-temperature machines with stationary racks

In either case, the maximum water temperature allowed is 194°F (90°C).

Chemical Sanitizing Machines

4-501-114

Using a lower water temperature mixed with chemicals is an effective final sanitization cycle in some dishwashing machines. The dishwashing machine manufacturer's instructions dictate the water temperature and chemical solution, which is automatically dispensed into the last rinse water. A chemical test kit verifies a good concentration, at least daily.

Dishwashing Manually

A three-compartment sink is used to comply with the Food Code's 3-step washing procedure, which includes washing, rinsing, and sanitizing. Warewashing sinks must not be used for handwashing.

Figure 7

Setting up a three-compartment sink:

1. Washing

- Clean and sanitize sinks and drain boards
- Pre-soak/pre-rinse all eating utensils and equipment
- Use clean, hot, soapy water at 110°F (43°C) or higher

4-501.19
4-603.14

2. Rinsing

- Use clean, hot water at 110°F (43°C) or higher

4-603-16

3. Sanitizing

- Use chemical solution and/or water temperature described earlier in this chapter
  - Use test strips to check the concentration
- Use appropriate immersion time
  - 7 seconds chlorine; 30 seconds quats or iodine
  - Always follow manufacturer's use directions

4-703.11

4. Air Dry

- Air dry utensils and equipment
- Do not stack wet items

4-904-14

Protection of Clean Items

Cleaned and sanitized equipment and food contact surfaces must be protected from contamination. The Food Code has specific requirements related to drying, lubricating, reassembling, storing, and generally preventing contamination of these items.

Drying

Equipment and utensils must be placed in a self-draining position that allows air drying and never towel-dried to avoid the possible transfer of microorganisms. Items may not be stacked until completely dry as wet-stacked items inhibit drying and may create an environment that supports bacterial growth.

Items must be air dried for a minimum time to ensure the chemical sanitizing solution is not transferred to a food or beverage.

Once utensils have dried, they may be polished with a cloth that is maintained clean and dry.

If cloths are air dried, they must not drip onto food or food-contact surfaces. The towels should be placed so that they will not become contaminated.

Lubricating and Reassembling

4-902

To properly maintain equipment, food-contact surfaces, and utensils, many of them require lubrication as directed by the manufacturer. In some cases, equipment must be disassembled. The Food Code requires that lubrication and reassembly be done in a manner that does not introduce contaminants to those surfaces.

Storing

4-903

When equipment, utensils, linens, and single-service and single-use articles have been cleaned and sanitized, they must be stored properly to prevent contamination.

Clean items shall be stored:

- In a clean, dry location
- Where they are not exposed to splash, dust, or other contamination
- At least 6 inches (15 cm) above the floor
- Flatware: in clean racks with handles up
- Cups: upside down in clean racks

See chapter 7 for additional storage details.

Cleaning the Facility

Keeping food-contact surfaces, equipment, linens, tableware, and utensils clean in a dirty building is challenging. Therefore, the food safety manager must ensure the facility is well maintained and clean to prevent cross-contamination. In addition to safe storage (chapter 7) and maintaining the facility and equipment (chapter 11), the Food Code requires non-food-contact surfaces to be cleaned at a frequency needed to prevent the accumulation of dirt and mold. Included are floors, walls, ceilings, plumbing fixtures, cabinets, etc.

Wiping Cloths

Towels are used throughout a food operation to keep everything clean and tidy. There are wet and dry towels; each has its purpose and should not be interchanged to prevent cross-contamination.

3-304.14

Wet Cloths

Wet cloths are kept in a unique cleaning bucket with a sanitizing solution. These cloths are used to wipe down tables and worksurfaces between uses. Due to ongoing use, the sanitizing solution must be replaced when it becomes heavily soiled or no longer meets the required concentration solution. The bucket should never be stored near food or cleaned and sanitized equipment.

Figure 8

Dry Cloths

A server's cloth, used for wiping food spills from tableware, must be maintained dry and not used for any other purpose.

Kitchen staff often keep a dry towel on their person to handle hot plates, pots, and pans. These towels may not be used to also clean up food spills.

Cloths that are maintained dry and clean may be used to polish cleaned and sanitized flatware.

Figure 9

Clean-up of Illness Events

When anyone in a food operation gets sick and vomits or has diarrhea, steps must be taken to properly clean the affected areas to prevent cross-contamination and food-borne illness. The *Norovirus* is often the cause and is highly contagious, so the response must be prompt. The Food Code requires a written plan to ensure the proper steps are taken during this sudden and dramatic event.

2-501.11

A written plan should consider:

- Close off, or segregate the affected area to limit cross-contamination
- Clean up of vomit or fecal matter and sanitization of affected surfaces
- Disposal of any exposed food being prepared or already served
- Availability and instruction on when/how staff should use PPE and disinfectants
- Procedures to dispose of or clean and sanitize cleaning tools and equipment used

Custodian Supplies

Figure 10

Custodian supplies should be stored separately from food storage in a dry and well-ventilated area. Mop sinks (or floor sinks) should be easy to access and well maintained. Wall-mounted mop hooks should be provided to store mops and allow them to air dry thoroughly. The mop hooks should be positioned above the floor sink to catch any dripping from drying mops.

Any hazardous products should be stored safely with intact product labels and, when possible, secured with limited access.

6-501.16

Notice, in the photo, the mop is hanging over the floor sink, and the hose attached to the faucet stops above the full water line of the sink.

Cleaning Schedule

Annex 3, 6-501.12

To ensure that cleaning is completed according to the minimum requirements of the Food Code, it is important to develop a cleaning schedule. When staff is trained on proper cleaning and sanitization steps and perform them according to a master schedule, it reduces the chances of these important tasks slipping through the cracks. Tracking these tasks with daily logs helps avoid the problem of someone thinking another person performed the required task. If a cleaning and sanitization task is not recorded in the log, it must be assumed not to have been completed and must be done.

Annex 5, Page 31

A food organization should develop a standard operating procedure (SOP) staff can refer to for reference. This written procedure must be kept on file and available for the inspector's review if they ask for it. The person in charge (PIC) must also be able to describe the process and training related to the cleaning schedule and SOP.

The following is an example of a cleaning and sanitizing SOP:

Cleaning and Sanitizing	
Why:	Remove bacteria or viruses that may cause foodborne illness from food contact surfaces.
Who:	Food workers
When:	When utensils, equipment or other food contact surfaces are used.
Where:	In food preparation areas.
How:	Clean and sanitize utensils and equipment: ☐ after each use ☐ every 4 hours if used to prepare TCS foods on a continuous basis Clean and sanitize utensils and equipment between preparing raw and ready to eat foods List your methods for sanitizing: Dishwashing ☐ Mechanical ☐ Manual | Sanitizer	Concentration	Water Temp | |---|---|---| | | | | | | | | Wiping Cloths | Sanitizer	Concentration	Water Temp | |---|---|---| | | | | | | | | ☐ _____
Optional Records:	☐ Cleaning and Sanitizing Schedule ☐ _____
Correction:	☐ Review records ☐ Re-clean / sanitize ☐ _____
PIC Verification:	● Verify that food contact surfaces are clean and sanitized ● Observe employee cleaning and sanitizing practices ● Check that dishwashing equipment is properly operated and maintained ● Use proper text kit or strips to verify sanitizer concentration or temperature

Figure 11

Summary

Cleaning and sanitizing food-contact surfaces, equipment, and utensils are essential to keeping food safe and preventing foodborne illness. A manager must understand the requirements, have a written plan, and be prepared to describe the standard operating procedures (SOP) to an inspector. Corrective actions should be taken, and retaining is given when staff is observed not cleaning and sanitizing correctly or at the required frequency.

Working with chemical sanitizers can be dangerous if mishandled or not used according to their instruction. Staff should have training and access to personal protective equipment (PPE).

Cleaning and sanitizing frequency:

- TCS food-contact surfaces: Every 4 hours or less
- Non-TCS food-contact surfaces: Every 24 hours or less

Basic cleaning and sanitizing steps:

- Washing
- Rinsing
- Sanitizing
- Air drying

Liquid temperatures:

Hot water only

- Hot water/heat sanitizing: 171°F (77°C) for 30 seconds
- Dishwashing machine: 180°F (82°C) or 165°F (74°C) for stationary racks

Water + chemical solution:

- Manual dishwashing: 110°
- Chemical concentrations:
- Chlorine   50-99 ppm,   7 seconds
- Iodine   12.5 – 25 ppm,   30 seconds
- Quats   Per manufacturer, 30 seconds, water hardness: 500 ppm or less

The Student's Workbook

As assigned by your instructor, use the separate Student's Workbook to work independently or in groups.

Activities for this week's chapter include:

- Discover what's lurking on your cellphone (bread petri dishes)
- Discover bacteria, yeast & mold visual characteristics
- Utilize best defrosting methods (recipe sauces)
- Understanding correct washing & sanitizing methods
- Watch the recipe video and reflect
- Discuss the risks of each ingredient in the lasagna recipe
- Make a list of equipment needed
- Produce the recipe
- Review the cleaning and sanitizing checklist
- End of chapter review video

Review Questions

Use these questions to check your knowledge of the material in this chapter. Your instructor has the answers.

1 The maximum time between cleaning TCS food-contact surfaces is:

a. 2 hours

b. 4 hours

c. 6 hours

d. 24 hours

2 The maximum time between cleaning non-TCS food-contact surfaces is:

a. 2 hours

b. 4 hours

c. 6 hours

d. 24 hours

3 Which is not a step in a manual dishwashing method:

a. Store

b. Rinse

c. Sanitize

d. Wash

4 Which is an acidic cleaning product:

a. Detergent

b. Abrasive cleaners

c. Degreaser

d. Delimer

5 The required minimum temperature in manual hot water sanitization is:

a. 171°F (77°C)

b. 180°F (82°C)

c. 165°F (74°C)

d. 110°F (43°C)

6 The acceptable concentration for iodine is:

a. 100 ppm

b. 50-99 ppm

c. 12.5 – 25 ppm

d. Per manufacturer

7 The minimum contact time for 50-99 ppm chlorine solution is:

a. 7 sec

b. 21 seconds

c. 30 seconds

d. 71 seconds

8 For a three-compartment sink, using a chemical sanitizer, the sanitize water temperature must be:

a. 171°F (77°C)

b. 180°F (82°C)

c. 110°F (43°C)

d. 165°F (74°C)

Chapter 11

Facility & Equipment

Introduction

A restaurant cannot be successful or comply with the Food Code with inadequate equipment or an improperly designed and maintained facility. A properly designed facility involves professional architects, engineers, foodservice consultants, and building and health officials. Careful planning and review go into developing the plans and specifications long before the construction teams start their work. This includes ensuring the building systems can support the intended use, including water pressure, hot water capacity, HVAC and ventilation, and electrical capacity and lighting intensity.

The equipment selection and investment are equally important. The equipment must be approved, durable, and easy to clean. Selecting the wrong equipment or trying to save money on a less powerful or lower-capacity item will lead to lower productivity and potentially underperforming food quality – maybe not unsafe but not satisfactory to the customer. Loss of revenue occurs when equipment needs to be prematurely replaced due to failure or an item does not meet the needs of an operation.

Key Terms

Keep an eye out for these essential topics:

- Construction documents
- Permit to operate
- Easily cleanable
- Cross-connection
- Backflow prevention
- Counter-mounted equipment
- American National Standards Institute (ANSI)
- NSF International

Objectives

After working through this chapter, you should be able to explain the following to friends and family:

- Appreciate the process necessary to design a restaurant
- Learn about a permit to operate and a certificate of occupancy
- Explore the facilities construction and material requirements
- Understand the required light intensity levels
- Describe the basic building systems (HVAC, electrical, and plumbing)
- Explain the installation requirements for food equipment

Andrea,
Executive Chef

The phone rang for what seemed the millionth time that day. Andrea, the Executive Chef of the Mockingbird Golf & Country Club, didn't feel like answering, but grabbed the receiver anyway. "Chef Andrea," she announced gruffly. The answer on the other end changed the day altogether. The local Houston water company informed her that the water would have to be switched off in just a few minutes. There was a chemical contamination concern in the area's water supply. What a disaster!

Her chefs were preparing for a large gala event the next day and had almost $100,000 worth of food in the kitchen storage for it. If there is no water, there can be no sanitation, toilets, or event. The afternoon was a whirlwind of discussions and heated moments as they dealt with the genuine implications of having to postpone the event for over 500 guests.

A few miles down the road about 15 minutes earlier, Juan was dealing with the issue head-on. He led a team of 10 experts in chemical pesticide applications. With mass farming in the United States, it is imperative that the growing crops aren't eaten by pests or destroyed by disease. Large parts of the country rely on the availability of affordable food grown in this way. Juan was filling the tanks of their machinery in the morning and noticed that the water pressure had dropped substantially. In the distance, he saw that a city utility worker had opened a flush valve, and water was gushing down the nearby street. In the tank he was filling was a Glyphosate compound, which he was diluting to the correct levels, with the hose all the way in the tank. Juan was very knowledgeable about the dangers of cross-connection backflow. He jumped into action when he noticed the levels in the tank going down, not up and shut off his water connection and disconnected his hose. He ran down to the utility worker to explain how he suspected, from the water pressure drop, that there was probably some back siphonage of the chemical into the water supply. Quick reactions and communications had to happen to shut off water supplies, flush pipes in the system, and alert the general public to the dangers. The contamination hurt no one, and life after a couple of days got back to normal, but the results could have been much worse if these competent individuals hadn't reacted promptly and with their expertise.

Two days later, Chef Andrea sat in her office with a hot cup of tea and breathed deeply. The gala just finished with a hugely successful dinner, with much applause for the staff's efforts to pull it off. On her desk, the local newspaper's headline story was about the city's narrow escape. Thank goodness she took that call, and thank goodness everyone was safe. Backflow contamination issues into a clean water supply can be catastrophic and hard to detect.

Physical Facilities

Architectural Design Process

The design of a new restaurant can vary greatly but must always involve a professional architectural design team to create **construction documents** (CDs) which are required drawings and specifications depicting the final building or operation. The CDs are then reviewed by the regulating authority and often bid on by contractors. The construction company awarded the project is then legally bound to provide nothing more and nothing less than what is in the construction documents. They must also provide proof of insurance in case they build something wrong or go out of business before the project is complete.

The design may start with an empty lot or be in an existing space, such as a shopping center or hotel. It may even be replacing a current restaurant. Several preliminary steps are required to ensure the location meets the various code requirements ranging from enough parking spaces to adequate square footage for all the rooms needed. In some cases, it may be determined that the lot or existing space cannot support the intended operation, which would not produce the necessary revenue, in which case the project may be scrapped.

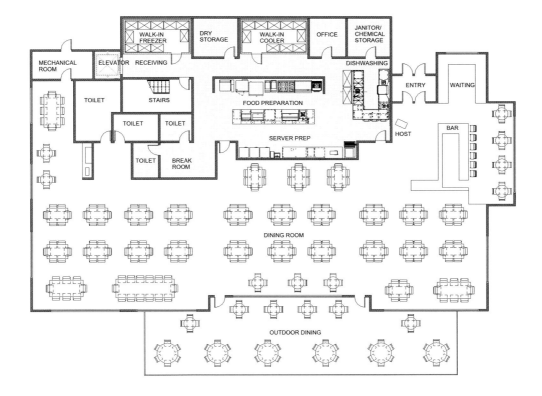

Figure 1

Design and Permitting

8-201

Once the design of a new food operation starts, the architectural design team will meet with the owner and end users to ensure their goals will be met in the subsequent design solution presented. This includes learning about the intended style (e.g., casual or formal) and what the menu will look like. All of this will dictate the spaces required and the equipment needed. The designers must also know if there will be a bar, outdoor seating, dancing, live music, and anything else that requires dedicated space, equipment, or power.

The design team will take the information gathered (think of this as puzzle pieces) and develop a design solution. The US has an international building code developed by the International Code Council (ICC), which many jurisdictions have adopted. Like the Food Code, this code is intended to protect public health in the case of things like fire and structural failures.

The exciting aspect of designing a new kitchen is the opportunity to implement new and more efficient equipment that can reduce the environmental impact compared to a similar operation. For example, an all-electric kitchen uses induction cooktops and heat pump-based water heaters, thus avoiding the consumption of fossil fuels.

Figure 2

Legal requirements

8-101.10

When the state, county, city, or tribal regulatory authority has adopted the FDA Food Code, it adheres to safeguard public health and to ensure that food is safe, unadulterated, and honestly presented when offered to the consumer or donated. These requirements, along with building codes and zoning regulations, directly influence the design of the building and, subsequently, the flow of food.

Plan review

8-201.11
Annex 2, Page 66

The regulating authority must review the architectural construction documents (CDs) to verify they meet the applicable regulations. If there are any problems, changing them on paper is a lot easier than once something is constructed incorrectly. When the design submission is approved, a construction permit is issued, and the selected contractor may begin construction.

Certificate of occupancy

During construction, only the contractor has unrestricted access to the site. For safety and insurance reasons, visitors, the owner, architect, and engineers must check in with the contractor when visiting the project during construction. Once construction is complete and the building and health departments sign off on the project, a certificate of occupancy is issued, and the owner may start using the building.

Permit to Operate a Food Establishment

In addition to the certificate of occupancy, the owner must apply for a **permit to operate** as a food establishment. Prior to receiving this permit, the business may not function as a food establishment. This is typically done with the county health department but can vary depending on location.

8-301

Once open, the restaurant is subject to surprise inspections, and serious violations could result in the suspension of the permit to operate, especially for any serious health risks. If the food operation intends to sell or serve alcohol, it must also apply for a permit to do so.

Spaces and Features

Regarding food operations, the Food Code requires rooms to be provided for specific functions. Some of these spaces also have required features, which will be touched on next.

Toilet rooms

Separate restrooms for customers and staff are ideal but not required. However, for combined use, customers may not be allowed to pass through a food preparation area.

Toilet rooms must be in a separate enclosed space with a tight-sealing door to minimize the movement of flies, insects, and rodents between the toilet room and food preparation areas. Toilet room doors may only be propped open during cleaning.

6-202.14

6-501.19

Additional requirements:

- Handwashing sinks — *can be adjacent to the toilet room*
- Toilet paper — *to minimize hand contact with fecal waste*
- Sanitary napkin receptacle — *in rooms used by females*

Toilet rooms must be cleaned regularly to limit the spread of microorganisms.

6-501.18

Storage areas

These are the storage spaces required by the Food Code. See chapter 7 for more on storage.

- Garbage
- Dry storage
- Refrigerated
- Frozen
- Hazardous
- Contaminated or recalled products

Figure 3

Electrical rooms

Any dedicated electrical room within the food operation should be locked and never used for storage. These rooms will contain power panels and electric equipment. Improper activities near electrical components can cause severe injury or death.

Exits

Annex 3, 6-202.15

Building codes require exits, and the Fire Marshall often inspects them to verify ongoing compliance. Exits, and approaches to them, should never be blocked with portable equipment, boxes, or other storage items. In the event of an emergency, staff and customers must have safe passage to any door or hallway with an exit sign.

Breakroom

6-403.11

A staff breakroom is not required, but it is good practice to provide one. Most food service workers are entitled to certain breaks. Having a place to sit and rest, and be out of the way of others working, is good for business.

This area is also where government-mandated informational posters are often displayed as well. This room is typically near the staff toilet rooms, lockers, and dressing rooms if they exist.

Lockers

8-305.11

Lockers (or similar) are required for staff clothing and personal belongings such as purses, coats, shoes, and personal medications. These items can contaminate food and equipment, which would be more likely to occur if staff did not have a place to store their things. Lockers also protect personal items from being stolen or used without permission.

Dressing rooms

8-305.11

Dressing rooms are required if staff routinely change clothes in the establishment. For example, some themed venues may not allow staff to take their work uniform (or costume) home, so staff must change on the premises.

Layout and Circulation

The layout of spaces -- and the flow of food -- must be carefully considered to ensure a smooth operation that limits the potential of cross-contamination. The layout shown on the previous page is an example of efficient circulation in the kitchen, where receiving and service staff activities do not cross paths with food preparation and dishwashing.

Construction Requirements

In addition to the building code, the Food Code has several requirements related to the construction and materials used in a food operation. In existing buildings, some existing features, e.g., walls, may need to be modified or replaced. There is no such thing as being "grandfathered in" within the Food Code.

A high-level concept that is important to understand is that floors, walls, and ceilings must be smooth, durable, and **easily cleanable**. Wall studs and floor joists or roof rafters/trusses may not be exposed in areas subject to moisture.

6-201

> **KEY TERM**
>
> **Easily cleanable** means a characteristic of a surface that:
>
> - Allows effective removal of soil by normal cleaning methods
> - Is dependent on the material, design, construction, and installation of the surface
> - Varies with the likelihood of the surface's role in introducing pathogenic or toxigenic agents or other contaminants into food based on the surface's approved placement, purpose, and use.

Floors

The restrictions and requirements related to floor finishes are designed to facilitate regular and effective cleaning and inhibit the potential for insect and rodent infestations.

Carpet

Where carpet is allowed, it must be closely woven and easily cleanable. The carpet must be securely attached to the floor and extended tightly to the walls and below the coving. Alternatively, the carpeting may stop short of the wall and must be secured with metal edge stripping or similar.

6-201.15

Carpeting is not allowed in the following areas:

- Food preparation areas
- Dishwashing areas
- Toilet rooms
- Garbage areas
- Any area subject to moisture

Nonabsorbent flooring

8-201.14

Nonabsorbent flooring is required in the areas where carpet is not allowed, such as food preparation areas, dishwashing, toilet rooms, garbage areas and any other areas that are subject to moisture.

Resilient flooring

Examples: Rubber tiles, Vinyl tile, and Vinyl sheet goods

Resilient flooring is a polymer-based material that offers a lower initial cost than hard-surface floor coverings. Resilient floors have some forgiveness on the smoothness of the subfloor beneath and offer some cushion when standing or dropping something on it. For some sheets goods, the flooring can turn up the wall, and inside/outside corners can be "welded" to create a highly waterproof solution.

Resilient flooring tends to be slippery when wet and less grease-resistant when compared to hard-surface flooring. The flooring is easier to scratch, but they are easily replaced in tiled locations. An inspector may cite a violation for missing tiles in a food production area.

Polymer flooring has a rather large embodied carbon footprint, making them not as environmentally friendly.

Hard-surface Flooring

Examples: Quarry tile, Ceramic tile, Terrazzo, Natural stone (marble, granite)

Hard-surface flooring is widely used in food preparation areas due to its durability and ease in keeping it clean. The product often comes with wall and floor tile options, with the latter being more slip-resistant. Given that these tiles have no flexibility, the subfloor must be very smooth, and the grout setting must account for the difference. Otherwise, the tiles will crack under the pressure of people walking on them.

Quarry tile flooring is very common in commercial kitchens. It comes with accessories like coved base, which creates a smooth transition from the floor tile to wall tile.

Mats and drainage tiles

Mats are sometimes placed at entry doors to prevent dust and dirt on the bottom of shoes from being tracked into the building. Drainage mats (duckboard) are used in unusually wet areas like dishwashing to prevent slipping. These mats must be removable and easy to clean to avoid accumulating dirt and waste and minimize the potential of contaminating food.

Outdoor surfaces

For outdoor walking and driving areas, the ground must be covered with concrete, asphalt, or gravel to minimize dust and facility maintenance and to prevent muddy conditions. These outdoor surface materials must be weather-resistant and handicap accessible per building codes. Exterior walking and driving surfaces shall be graded to drain rainwater and melting snow to drains, inlets, or holding areas.

When cleaning is accomplished by spraying or flushing, the juncture between the floor and wall must be coved. Doing so prevents water from pooling and harboring insects, which can cause bacterial growth, such as *Listeria monocytogenes*.

Walls and Ceilings

Wall and ceiling covering materials shall be attached to be easily cleanable. Any attachments to a wall or ceiling must be easily cleanable, except in consumer areas where decorative items are kept clean.

Any exposed concrete or concrete block walls must be finished and sealed to ensure a smooth and easily cleanable surface, except in areas dedicated to dry storage.

6-201.16

Exterior openings

Outer openings shall be protected against the entry of insects and rodents. Windows must be tight fitting and have insect screens if operable. Doors must be closed and tight-fitting. These requirements do not apply to openings that open into a larger structure, such as a shopping center or airport. All holes and penetrations in the building must be adequately sealed.

6-202.15

The Life Safety Code does not require exterior doors used as exits to be self-closing, but they can be. In the National Fire Protection Association's NFPA 101, Life Safety Code, 2009 Edition, doors to exit enclosures such as stairs, horizontal exits, or exit passageways are required to be self-closing.

Outdoor Garbage Areas

Outdoor garbage (refuse) areas shall be constructed according to code. They must also have a curb built around the perimeter and have a sloped floor surface to collect and contain anything that might leak from the accumulated trash until it is hauled away.

6-202.110

Building Systems (MEP)

The mechanical, electrical, and plumbing (MEP) systems must be able to support the intended use, including water pressure, hot water capacity, HVAC and ventilation, and electrical capacity and lighting intensity.

Water

Water is critical to any food operation. It is used to wash hands and dishes, as an ingredient in food, to cook food, and as a beverage. Therefore the building's water supply must be drinkable (potable) and have adequate pressure for the intended use and capacity of the operation.

Water Supply

5-101

Potable water (drinking water) must be obtained from an approved source, such as:

- A public water system
- A private water system
- Water transport vehicles
- Water containers

A private water system must comply with the law and state drinking water quality standards. Bottled drinking water may be used if received from an approved source. After an emergency situation involving the building's water supply, the system must be flushed and disinfected before being returned to service.

The food manager should know the qualities of the water, such as hardness. This will aid in scheduling descaling tasks as well as meeting chemical sanitization solutions requirements.

If an approved non-drinking water system exists, such as a greywater system for flushing toilets and urinals, it shall not be used for anything else.

Hot Water

Hot water is necessary to run an effective food operation; it is used regularly, from handwashing to sanitizing solutions and more. Some equipment can make hot water, such as dishwashing machines, some clothes washing machines, and heat boosters within sinks. Other applications draw hot water from a hot water heater.

The water heater's location and tank size will determine how responsive it is and if it can meet the required demand. Because they have a limited life span, water heaters should be inspected regularly. When they fail, they have the potential to flood a space, especially if it happens when no one is present, like overnight.

Plumbing

Beyond the building code, the Food Code has many requirements and restrictions related to the building's plumbing system.

To prevent leaks and condensation from contaminating food, pipes may not be unnecessarily exposed. Their placement cannot prevent or inhibit cleaning when they must be exposed.

Water conditioning and backflow prevention devices must be accessible for regular maintenance and service.

The overall plumbing system must be maintained in good repair and repaired according to law.

Handwashing sinks

There must be at least one sink, but enough for convenient use by staff; or the minimum number required by local ordinances, building code, or law. They must remain accessible to employees at all times, meaning they should never be blocked by portable equipment, delivered goods, etc.

Each handwashing sink or group of handwashing sinks must have:

6-301

1. Hand cleaning liquid, powder, or bar soap (one per two sinks minimum)
2. Hand drying provisions
3. Waste receptacle (if disposable towels are used)
4. Handwashing signage (one per sink)

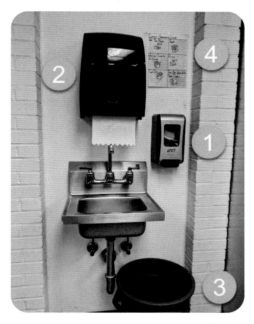

Figure 4

5-202.12

Handwashing sinks should have ample warm water, as it is more effective than cold water in removing fatty residue often associated with food preparation. The required temperature, starting with the 2022 Food Code, is 85°F (29.4°C).

Sinks must be used only for their intended purpose. Sinks used to wash hands should not be used to wash pots. Conversely, sinks used for food preparation or utensil washing may not be used for handwashing. In fact, those sinks are not allowed to have the handwashing aids and devices listed above (hand soap, towels, signage).

A sign or poster is required to remind food employees to wash their hands.

Toilets and Urinals

The minimum number of toilets and urinals required by local ordinances, building code, or law.

5-203.12

Service Sink

At least one service sink (mop sink or floor sink) or curbed cleaning facility shall be provided. The floor sink is used to clean mops or similar wet floor cleaning tools and for the disposal of mop water and similar liquid waste.

5-203.13

Toilets, urinals, and other sinks must never be used at a service sink or to dispose of mop water.

Service sinks should be cleaned and sanitized at least every 24 hours and immediately after cleaning up a vomit or diarrhea event.

Cross-connections

5-205.12

The Food Code prohibits connecting a pipe, or similar, from the building's water supply to another system (e.g., non-drinking water or of unknown water quality). A **cross-connection** would result in the contamination of the building's potable water supply.

Backflow Prevention

5-402.11

The building's plumbing system must be designed to prevent backflow, which can contaminate the water supply. **Backflow prevention** is accomplished with a backflow prevention device or an air gap.

Backflow happens when the water supply piping comes into contact with wastewater (or sewage). For example, consider this improper design and restricted activity:

- A hose is attached to a sink faucet to fill a mop bucket
- The mop bucket has a chemical sanitizer in it
- The end of the hose is submerged in the bucket
- Due to high water demand in the area/building, a sudden drop in the water pressure occurs
- Mop water is siphoned through the hose into the water supply pipes
- The building's water supply is now contaminated and unsafe to use

A similar problem can occur in a full sink with an improperly installed faucet or spray hose that extends below the water line in a full sink. A backflow prevention device or air gap will prevent (or minimize) water supply contamination.

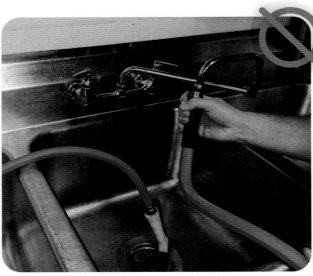

Figure 5

Figure 6

As shown in the photo, an air gap is the only fail-safe way to prevent backflow between the building's water supply and the sewage piping.

Floor drains do connect directly to the building's sewage system, as they are an integral part of the plumbing system.

Sewage

The building sewage must be disposed of legally, which usually means it goes through the sewage pipes to a public sewage treatment plant. Alternatively, an adequately sized sewage holding tank is installed (usually below ground) and pumped and removed by a specialized professional service.

5-401.11

Grease traps prevent grease from entering sewage piping and causing a blockage. If used, they must be easily accessible for cleaning.

HVAC

The heating, ventilation, and air conditioning (HVAC) system is essential to the comfort and safety of any building. The HVAC system must be designed, installed, and balanced so that make-up air, intake air, and exhaust vents do not cause condensation or food contamination. Exhaust and intake louvers must be spaced far enough apart to prevent cross-contamination of air. Intakes should also be placed away from receiving areas where the exhaust from delivery trucks may be pulled into the building.

6-202.12

Ventilation

If necessary, provide mechanical ventilation of sufficient capacity to keep rooms free of excessive heat, steam, condensation, vapors, obnoxious odors, smoke, and fumes.

6-304.11

Exhaust hoods and exhaust vents in storage rooms and restrooms should be installed per code. Greese filters must be removable for replacement and equipment cleaning.

4-301.14
4-202.18

Electrical

The building's electrical system must be installed according to code. This includes many safety measures to keep people safe, such as ground fault circuit interrupt (GFCI) in areas that may get wet. The manager should be aware of the safety precautions related to the electrical system and train staff as needed. Electrical rooms should be secured and never used for storage.

Lighting

Lighting serves many purposes in a food operation. Lighting is essential, from creating an atmosphere in the dining rooms to clear and safe visibility in the kitchen. In addition to building code requirements about minimum average illuminance and emergency lighting levels, the Food Code also has crucial conditions that must be met to help keep staff and food safe.

6-303

A light meter measures light intensity, which relates to how bright or dark a space is. Some areas, such as the dining room, are intentionally darker for the atmosphere.

In spaces where a consumer selects food (e.g., a buffet or salad bar) and areas in which food is prepared (e.g., working with a knife), there must be enough light to see and safely operate.

Space Type	Light Level Minimum	Workplane Height
Storage, walk-in cooler	10 fc (108 lux)	30 inches (75 cm)
Self-service	20 fc (215 lux)	At food surface
Inside equipment (e.g. reach-in refrig)		Inside equipment
Handwashing, dishwashing		30 inches (75 cm)
Toilet rooms		30 inches (75 cm)
Food preparation areas	50 fc (540 lux)	At working surface

Figure 7

Keep in mind these are minimums - the average light intensity recommended by the Illuminating Engineering Society (IES) for a commercial kitchen is 50-100 fc (540-1076 lux). During the facility's design, lighting designers can simulate the light levels using software, as shown in the example below.

Good lighting aids in visually inspecting food, reading labels, using a knife, and cleaning.

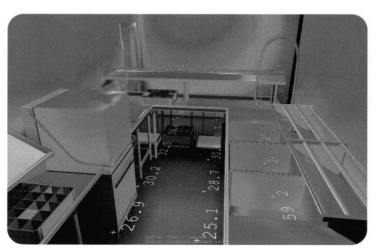

Figure 8

Light bulbs near food and food-contact surfaces must be shielded or shatterproof to avoid food contamination from glass fragments. This requirement does not apply to storage areas containing food in unopened packages.

Foodservice Equipment

The equipment used in a food operation must be high-quality, heavy-duty, and commercial-grade to hold up to repeated use, washing, and a few bumps here and there. By contrast, the equipment used in a private residence is not nearly as durable and would not hold up to repeated use, and would be, in fact, unsafe to try.

Foodservice equipment can have hot, sharp, or moving parts as well as high-powered motors. This is one of the reasons staff are not allowed to wear jewelry. In addition to the potential of contaminating food, jewelry can get caught in active equipment and seriously harm the person wearing it and/or damage the equipment. Therefore, staff must be trained on how to properly use any equipment they need to use for the tasks they have been assigned.

> **KEY TERM**
>
> **Equipment** means an article that is used in the operation of a food establishment such as a freezer, grinder, hood, ice maker, meat block, mixer, oven, reach-in refrigerator, scale, sink, slicer, stove, table, temperature measuring device for ambient air, vending machine, or warewashing machine. This does not include apparatuses used for handling or storing large quantities of packaged foods that are received from a supplier in a cased or overwrapped lot, such as hand trucks, forklifts, dollies, pallets, racks, and skids.
>
> **Counter-mounted equipment** means equipment that is not portable and is designed to be mounted off the floor on a table, counter, or shelf.

Standards

The Food Code lists specific characteristics for the materials and construction of foodservice equipment. The equipment may not transfer any substance, color, order, or tastes to the food.

Under normal use, the equipment shall be:

- Safe
- Sufficient in weight and thickness to withstand repeated dishwashing
- Finished to have a smooth, easily cleanable surface
- Resistant to pitting, chipping, scratching, and decomposition

4-101.11

There are several limitations to materials that can be used in food preparation. For example, cast iron may only be used as a cooking surface, and copper and galvanized metal cannot be used with acid foods. Additionally, nonstick-coated cooking surfaces may only be used with non-scratching utensils.

4-101.12

Food equipment must be certified or classified for sanitation by an **American National Standards Institute (ANSI)**-accredited certification program.

4-205.10

NSF International is a popular and widely recognized ANSI-accredited program in the US. Products that have been independently tested by NSF will have their logo on it, as shown in the photo.

Figure 9

7-203.11

A container previously used to store poisonous or toxic materials may not be used to store, transport, or dispense food, equipment, utensils, linens, single-service, or single-use articles.

Fixed Equipment: Spacing

In addition to the equipment being easy to clean, fixed equipment must also be installed so that it is easy to clean around it.

Fixed equipment installation requirements:

- Spaced to allow access for cleaning along the sides, behind, and above the equipment
- Maximum spacing of **1/32 inch** (1 mm) from adjoining equipment, walls, and ceilings

  or

- Sealed to adjoining equipment or walls if the equipment is exposed to spillage or seepage

Counter-mounted equipment requirements:

- Sealed

  or

- Elevated on legs per the next section

Fixed Equipment: Elevation or Sealing

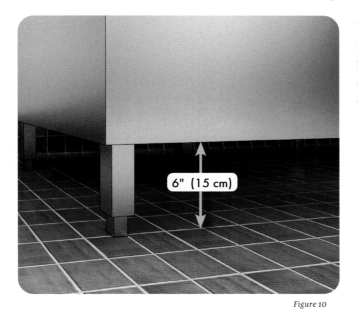

Figure 10

Fixed floor-mounted equipment must be raised a minimum of **6 inches** (15 cm) above the floor or sealed tight to facilitate cleaning and prevent bacterial growth.

4-402.11(A)

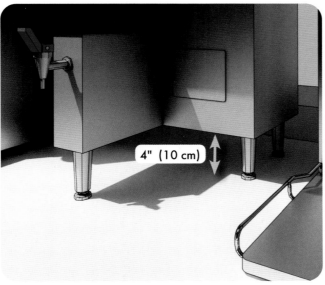

Figure 11

Because it is easier to access, fixed counter-mounted equipment must only be raised **4 inches** (10 cm) above the countertop.

4-402.11(D)

The clearance space between the table and counter-mounted equipment may be:

4-402.11(E)

- 3 inches (7.5 cm) if the horizontal distance of the table top under the equipment is no more than 20 inches (50 cm) from the point of access for cleaning; or

- 2 inches (5 cm) if the horizontal distance of the table top under the equipment is no more than 3 inches (7.5 cm) from the point of access for cleaning

Equipment must be kept in good repair or replaced to avoid accidents or cross-contamination. For example, heavy grooves in a cutting board can be difficult to properly clean and sanitize.

Annex 3, Page 171
Annex 7, Page 42

Summary

A well-designed and properly maintained food operation, with approved and quality equipment, are the ingredients for a successful business that can comply with the Food Code requirements. This all starts with a professional design team and the production of drawings and specifications, followed by a building and health inspector review. The final approved project receives a certificate of occupancy and a permit to operate as a food establishment.

The building systems must be able to accommodate the demand of the operation, from water pressure and temperature to adequate ventilation and plumbing to electrical capacity and lighting intensities. Additionally, the water supply must be from an approved source, protected from contamination with backflow prevention, and never allow a cross-connection to any other system.

The foodservice equipment must be from an ANSI accredited program, such as NSF International, which independently tests and approves food preparation equipment for safe use and cleanability. Approved equipment should bear the NSF label.

Chapter numbers review:

- Water temperature at a handwashing sink: 100°F to 108°F (38°C - 42°C).
- Light intensity levels: 10, 20, and 50 fc (108, 215, and 540 lux)
- Maximum equipment spacing from adjacent walls/equipment: 1/32" (1 mm)
- Equipment height:
  - 6" (15 cm) above a floor
  - 4" (10 cm) above a countertop

The Student's Workbook

As assigned by your instructor, use the separate Student's Workbook to work independently or in groups.

Activities for this week's chapter include:

- Make group presentations on the 6 BIG pathogens
- Watch the video and reflect
- Discuss the risks of each ingredient in the focaccia recipe
- Make a list of equipment needed
- Produce the recipe
- Review the cleaning and sanitizing checklist
- Fill out the recipe and cost form
- End of chapter review video

Use these questions to check your knowledge of the material in this chapter. Your instructor has the answers.

1 Which is not a requirement for floors, walls, and ceilings construction?

a. Durable

b. Thick

c. Smooth

d. Easily cleanable

2 Which is not a resilient floor?

a. Vinyl tile

b. Rubber tiles

c. Vinyl sheet goods

d. Ceramic tile

3 A popular floor covering in food preparation areas is:

a. Quarry tile

b. Wood

c. Brick

d. Marble

4 When in a food preparation area, toilet rooms must:

a. Be open, with a protected line of sight

b. Have multiple stalls

c. Be unisex

d. Be fully enclosed with walls and a door

5 Water may not come from:

a. A well

b. A private water system

c. A water transport vehicle

d. A public water system

6 Which is not a requirement of a handwashing sink:

a. Accessible, not blocked

b. It cannot be used to wash dishes

c. Must have a hands-free faucet

d. Must have a sign

7 The only fail-safe way to prevent backflow into a water system:

a. Air gap

b. Water hammer device

c. Backflow prevention device

d. Use a cross-connection

8 Equipment mounted on a countertop must be elevated:

a. 6 inches (15 cm)

b. 3 inches (8 cm)

c. 4 inches (10 cm)

d. 2 inches (5 cm)

Chapter 12

Pest Control

Introduction

In addition to the fact that customers do not like seeing insects or rodents while dining, these tiny creatures carry disease and can contaminate food and food-contact surfaces. Steps must be taken to minimize their presence.

Understanding the various pests to watch out for and how they find their way into a facility is required in order to effectively monitor and control their activity. Additionally, outdoor areas such as dining or trash storage areas require special attention as well.

When pests show, a prepared plan must be enacted to safely manage the problem in and around food. This requires an integrated pest management (IPM) plan and will benefit from a professional pest control operator (PCO). When using and storing toxic chemicals on the premises, there are some specific rules to follow for employee safety and consumer health.

Key Terms

Keep an eye out for these essential topics:

- Pests
- Service animal
- Infestation
- Air curtain

- Sealed
- Integrated Pest Management (IPM)
- Pest control operator (PCO)
- Pesticide

Objectives

After working through this chapter, you should be able to explain the following to friends and family:

- Learn about the kinds of pests to watch for
- Explore the problem areas inside and outside an operation
- Understand how to create an integrated pest management (IPM) program
- Describe the benefits of working with a pest control operator (PCO)
- Explain the storage and use requirements related to poisonous and toxic materials

Robert,
Pest Control Operator

Robert is very good at his job. Many see it as a temporary job on the way to something better. For Robert, it was something that was fascinating and totally science-based, which he always enjoyed. Robert is a licensed Pest Control Operator. He works for a national company's local office, which is very well equipped for all eventualities and has excellent training programs as well. Robert entered his career soon after high school. He was interested in studying biology in college but decided it wasn't right for him halfway into his first semester. Instead, he attended his local state structural pest control registered technician school. After an in-depth study course, he started work and learned the ropes from the licensed technician he worked under.

What Robert loves most is to re-train business owners to think carefully about how to stop pests from entering their business and how best to eradicate them if they get in. Robert sees himself as an educator. He spends many hours of the day working with clients to help them stop the problem of pests at the source, such as explaining how best to store foods off the floor on metal shelving at least six inches off the ground, and the need for hinged floor grates, properly sealed doors, and working window screens.

After working for his company for several years, Robert has had several promotions and earns a very healthy living. His local branch doesn't really spend money on marketing their services, as word of mouth travels, and the best in the business is in high demand. Robert feels pretty confident that he will be in this job until it's time to retire.

References in this Coursebook:

Glossary reference: Orange text means the definition of the word can be found in the Glossary located in the Student Workbook.

Food Code section reference: To verify or further study topics covered in this Coursebook, the FDA Food Code section numbers are provided in the margins. The current version of the offical code may be download here: https://www.fda.gov/food/retail-food-protection/fda-food-code

Types of Pests & Rodents

Many types of pests can cause problems for a food establishment. The most prevalent pest type can vary by geographic area, type of food establishment, building construction, exterior lighting, and cleaning practices. These small to microscopic living things can carry diseases, infest stored products, as well as contaminate.

The Food Code specifically mentions pests, insects, and rodents. The word "**pests**" ia a catchall word to describe any undesirable and destructive insect or animal within the food operation. It is helpful to know a little about the most problematic pests in a food operation to understand better how to monitor and control them.

Rodents

Rats and mice are the most common type of rodents. They typically nest within walls or other concealed areas--another reason floor-mounted equipment must be raised or sealed to floors and walls. They are nocturnal, so they naturally only come out at night unless hungry — customers do not like to see these little creatures!

Rodents present a severe health risk as they carry diseases (e.g., *E. Coli*, *Salmonella*, *Listeria*), destroy products by gnawing through packaging and eating stored food products, and contaminate food and food-contact surfaces with their feces and when they die. They cause other problems when they chew through electrical wiring and building materials.

Rats

- Range from nest: 100 — 150 feet (30 — 46 m)
- Hole size: Half dollar-sized
- Reach: 18 inches

Mice

- Range from nest: 10 - 30 feet (3 — 9 m)
- Hole size: nickel-sized

Figure 1

Flies

Figure 2

Flies are not just a nuisance to staff and customers, as they can carry and spread hundreds of diseases (e.g., Shigella spp.). Flies are attracted to food, predominantly liquid food. They can only eat liquid food but are able to dissolve solid food by vomiting on it and sucking the vomit back up using their straw-shaped tongue. Additionally, their waste matter and the flies themselves (when they die or get trapped in food) will contaminate food and surfaces.

Cockroaches

Figure 3

Cockroaches exist nearly everywhere. Most live in the natural environment, but some find their way into buildings and cause a public health issue, especially in food establishments. One of the problems is that before they walk across sanitized surfaces or unadulterated food, they have most certainly spent time in the trash, contaminated water, or mold and mildew found in hard-to-clean areas. Roaches carry many bad bugs, such as *Salmonella* (bacteria) and *Hepatitis* (virus) which can lead to foodborne illness.

When cockroaches move around, they leave filth, including an oily substance that produces an unpleasant odor. This activity contaminates food, food-contact surfaces, plates, cups, and utensils that are otherwise thought to be sanitized.

In addition to this disease-causing contamination, some people are allergic to the substances roaches leave behind; for some, the problem is ingesting contaminated food, while others are affected by inhaling dried airborne fecal matter. The big challenge is all of this contamination happens overnight, in the dark, while no one is watching.

Here are a few usual places to look for cockroaches:

- Dark, sheltered areas
- Kitchen sinks or drain boards
- Plumbing and water heaters
- Gaps below or around cabinets and equipment
- Where pipes and conduit penetrate walls
- Behind door or window frames
- Behind wall base, trim, and more

In these areas, look for a black pepper-like or coffee ground-looking substance, which is a sign of pest activity or infestation. Another telltale sign is capsule-shaped eggs. This is a sign of cockroach waste, which requires immediate action.

Insects

Figure 4

Many types of insects can find their way into stored or packaged products, such as beetles, moths, weevils, mites, etc. They have plenty of food and refuge where they multiply, excrete waste, and die.

The entry points might happen long before arrival, at the food processing plant where flour, grain, nuts, or other products are packaged, or during transit. They can also enter while in storage in the food establishment.

When these pests contaminate the food, they can cause foodborne illness or allergic reactions when consumed. Therefore, close inspection during receiving, regular monitoring of storage spaces, and proper product rotation are critical in the early detection or prevention of pest infestations.

Service Animals

Annex 2, Page 278

Figure 5

While pets are prohibited from food establishments, service animals are an exception and are not considered pets. This exception is a right afforded by the Americans with Disabilities Act (ADA) which prevents privately owned businesses that serve the public from discriminating against individuals with disabilities.

2-403.11

The service animal can accompany the customer anywhere customers can generally go. However, service animals (of an employee or customer) are not allowed in food preparation areas. Employees with service animals must wash their hands after each contact to remove dirt and pathogens.

6-501.115
Annex 3, Page 507

Starting with the 2022 Food Code, if approved by the regulatory authority, food establishments may allow pet dogs in outdoor dining areas. Food employees are not allowed to touch pet dogs or any other animal that may be present, e.g. patrol dogs.

> **KEY TERM** **Service animal** means an animal such as a guide dog, signal dog, or other animal individually trained to provide assistance to an individual with a disability.

Aquariums

Fish aquariums, molluscan shellfish, or crustacea display tanks are allowed in customer areas. Employees must wash their hands after handling or caring for them or the equipment.

Taking Precautions

6-501.111

The Food Code prohibits the accumulation of trash and unnecessary equipment inside and outside the food establishment to avoid attracting and creating harborage for insects and rodents. The overall upkeep and cleanliness of the operation are essential to preventing an **infestation**, which is a significant number of pests established in a given area.

The key precautions are:

- Prevent access to the facility
- Careful inspection during receiving
- Limit places to hide and nest
- Minimize food and water access
- Create an integrated pest management (IPM) program
- Work with a professional pest control operator (PCO)

Exterior Areas

There are several pest control-related precautions to take outside the food establishment.

Outdoor Dining

Tables and chairs should be wiped between parties, and the ground should be maintained free of food. The ground surface should be paved and easily cleanable, and not dirt. Customers should be consistently instructed not to feed any animals or birds.

Bird deterrents should be added to places birds might otherwise sit and watch for falling food, especially over/above dining areas.

Lighting

Lighting must be well designed to provide customers safety and avoid attracting insects as much as possible. This can be done by implementing proper outdoor light levels significantly lower than interior lighting requirements. Minimizing the light shining on the building and focusing on the walking and driving areas will help keep insects and rodents away from the building.

Trash storage

Trash storage areas must be easy to clean and contain any liquid runoff. The capacity of the trash storage should be sized based on the operation volume and the frequency of trash removal by the service provider. Doing so will avoid overflow, which would surely attract insects and rodents. Ideally, to help maintain a clean space, the outdoor trash area and dumpsters should be cleaned after each trash pickup.

Exterior openings

Exterior crack

Exterior hole

Figure 6

Doors, windows, gaps, and cracks are the main entry points for pests. Doors and windows should be closed at all times, and tight fitting. Open windows must have an insect screen. Doors and drive-through windows that are opened and closed often can benefit from an **air curtain**, which is installed above the door and blows a heavy stream of air across the opening when opened.

The perimeter of all penetrations into the building should be inspected multiple times a year for gaps or cracks and **sealed** with caulk as needed. This includes any above-ground pipes, conduits, cable television wires, doors, and windows.

KEY TERM   **Sealed** means free of cracks or other openings that allow the entry or passage of moisture or pests.

Interior Areas

There are several pest control-related precautions to take inside the food establishment.

Dining

Tables and chairs should be wiped between parties, and the floor should be maintained free of food. Spills should be cleaned up quickly, especially in carpeted areas. All aspects of the dining room should be continually cleaned to avoid the accumulation of filth and mold. This can be tricky or time-consuming in themed restaurants with elaborate decorations but must be done to prevent attracting pests.

Food Preparation

This book has an entire chapter on cleaning and sanitizing (chapter 10), focusing mainly on food preparation areas. The main goal of cleaning is to avoid contamination, which is also a goal of pest control measures.

Receiving and Storage

6-501.111(A)

Incoming shupments should be routinely inspected for signs of pests or pest activities.

The storage of food, covered in chapter 7, has several requirements that aim to minimize pests' attraction and harborage. For example, food items must be stored at least 6 inches (15 cm) above the ground. This facilitates cleaning and reduces places for pests to hide and nest. Limiting the long-term duration of an item in storage (using the FIFO method) and storing foods in tightly sealed containers goes a long way in preventing pest infestations.

Trash

6-501.114

Within the building, trash receptacles must be emptied regularly to avoid overflow, which attracts insects and rodents. Trash containers and areas around them must be cleaned regularly.

Floor Drains

Flies and other pests can live within floor drains. They should be checked regularly and cleaned to prevent pests from finding refuge in floor drains.

Integrated Pest Management (IPM) Program

Integrated Pest Management **(IPM)** is a science-based process that uses biological, environmental, and technological information to manage pest damage to minimize economic costs and risks to people, property, and the environment.

Figure 7

An IPM program is designed to:

- Keep pests from entering the premises
- Prevent unacceptable levels of pest damage
- Minimize health risks to people, property, and the environment

Optimal results are obtained working with a professional **pest control operator (PCO)** when developing an IPM program. These specialists have specific training and experience in preventing pest entry and dealing with infestations safely within a food operation.

Insects, rodents, and other pests shall be controlled by:

- Inspecting deliveries of food and supplies
- Routinely inspecting the premises for evidence of pests
- Using methods, if pests are found, such as traps or other means of pest control
- Eliminating harborage conditions

When insect control devices are used, they must be designed to contain the insect and be positioned so they are not over or near a food preparation area or food-contact surfaces. Any dead or trapped birds, insects, rodents, and other pests must be removed from trapping devices and the premises as needed to prevent their accumulation, decomposition, and the attraction of pests.

6-501.111(C)

6-501.112

The PIC must be able to explain the integrated pest management (IPM) program to an inspector and show logs, pest traps, and related chemicals stored on the premises. The following is an example of a daily pest control management log.

Pest Management Log	M A/R	T A/R	W A/R	T A/R	F A/R
Trash, Debris, and Garbage					
Evidence of Rodents, Flies, and Birds					
Rodent Glue Traps					
Use and Storage of Pest Control Substances					
Initials					
Notes					
Date: _____ / _____ / _____ Initials _____ (passes examination)					

Poisonous or toxic materials

As previously covered in chapter 7 (Storage) and chapter 10 (Cleaning and Sanitization), poisonous and toxic chemicals are dangerous. They must be used and stored properly to keep staff and food safe.

When working with toxic chemicals:

- The pesticide label is the law, and the label instructions must be followed.
- The manufacturer's label must indicate that the product can be used in a food establishment.

Annex 4, Page 16

- Have a **Safety Data Sheet (SDS)** on file for any products stored on the premises
- Insect traps (sticky traps, light traps, electric traps) and covered tamper-resistant bait stations are acceptable and can be used in a facility if placed correctly.

7-206.12

- Traps and bait stations must be placed in areas that are not above food, equipment, utensils, linens, and single-service or single-use articles.

7-206.13

- Tracking powers may not be used in a food establishment.

> **KEY TERM**
> **Poisonous or toxic materials** means substances that are not intended for ingestion.

Poisonous or toxic materials are included in 4 categories:

- Cleaners and sanitizers, which include cleaning and sanitizing agents and agents such as caustics, acids, drying agents, polishes, and other chemicals
- Pesticides, except sanitizers, which include substances such as insecticides and rodenticides
- Substances necessary for the operation and maintenance of the establishment such as nonfood grade lubricants and personal care items that may be deleterious to health
- Substances that are not necessary for the operation and maintenance of the establishment and are on the premises for retail sale, such as petroleum products and paints.

Figure 8

Ideally, if not covered and self-contained, applied pest control chemicals will be used when the operation is closed and food-contact surfaces and equipment are covered to prevent contamination.

Pesticide is a toxic substance that kills pests upon contact, or when they eat it. Some are designed to be carried back to the nest and kill the colony. A pesticide is only allowed if the label lists restaurants, and similar food handling establishments as use areas, like the following example.

7-202

Insecticide

FOR USE IN RESIDENTIAL, INSTITUTIONAL, COMMERCIAL, AND INDUSTRIAL AREAS

Use sites include single and multi-family residential building, schools, commerical and industrial facilities (including warehouses, apartments, supermarkets, restaurants, motels, hotels, hospitals, food handling/ storage establishments), and transportation equipment such as aircraft, trains, ships, boats, and buses.

Active ingredient:
Indoxacarb:
(S)-methyl 7-chloro-2,5-dithrou-2-[[(methoxycarbonyl) [4-(trifluoromethoxy)phenyl]amino]carbonyl] indeno[1,2-e] [1,3,4]oxadiazine-4a-(3H)carboxylate   0.6%

Other ingredients   99.4%

Total   100.0%

Figure 9

A pesticide is not allowed if the label says "For Indoor Residential Use Only."

From the Food Code:

Annex 5, Page 26

During each inspection, the proper labeling, storage, and use of poisonous and toxic chemicals should be verified. Containers of poisonous or toxic materials and personal care items shall bear a legible manufacturer's label. Working containers used for storing poisonous or toxic materials such as cleaners and sanitizers taken from bulk supplies should be clearly and individually identified with the common name of the material. Only chemicals that are necessary to the operation and maintenance of a food establishment, such as for the cleaning and sanitizing of equipment and utensils and the control of insects and rodents, should be in the food establishment. Medicines necessary for the health of employees may be allowed in a food establishment, but they should be labeled and stored to prevent contamination of food and food-contact surfaces.

Summary

In a food establishment, pests mustn't be allowed to enter or multiply within the facility easily. If they do, they pose a severe public health concern as food becomes contaminated and can result in foodborne illness or an allergic reaction when consumed.

An integrated pest management (IPM) program defines a process that monitors for pest activity and defines a timely response when an infestation is identified. Working with a professional pest control operator (PCO) is also beneficial to ensure safe and effective methods are used. Pesticides can be dangerous for employees to handle, and they can also contaminate food if carelessly misused.

Steps to properly manage pests:

- Eliminate all openings, cracks, and gaps in your building
- Inspect products at receiving for insects or rodents, including signs of activity or damage
- Store pesticides in their original packaging
- Apply pesticides only per the label
- Store pesticides separate from food and food-contact surfaces
- Hire a professional pest control operator (PCO) to apply pesticides
- Pets are prohibited from food production areas and largely prohibited from food service establishments (except dogs in approved outdoor dining areas)
- Fish aquariums and service animals for the disabled are permitted in customer areas only

The Student's Workbook

As assigned by your instructor, use the separate Student's Workbook to work independently or in groups.

Activities for this week's chapter include:

- Play the signs of infestion game
- Watch the video and reflect
- Discuss the risks of each ingredient in the rice recipe
- Make a list of equipment needed
- Produce the one pot chicken & rice recipe
- Review the cleaning and sanitizing checklist
- Fill out the recipe and cost form

Review Questions

Use these questions to check your knowledge of the material in this chapter.
Your instructor has the answers.

1 Which of the following are allowed in regular indoor customer areas?

a. Pets
b. Service Animals
c. Uncovered bait stations
d. Overflowing trash

2 How far does a mouse travel from its nest?

a. 100 – 150 feet (30 – 46 m)
b. 100 – 159 feet (3 – 46 m)
c. No limit
d. 10 - 30 feet (3 – 9 m)

3 Which is not a pest control precaution:

a. Increase spacing between dining room tables
b. Limit places to hide
c. Prevent access to the facility
d. Minimize access to food and water

4 Which is the plan used to monitor and prevent pests:

a. Sanitation control plans
b. Pest monitoring and prevention plan
c. Pest control operator
d. Integrated pest management

5 Outdoor trash enclosures must:

a. Contain any liquid
b. Be covered to keep water out
c. Be painted green
d. Have at least three walls and a gate

6 Which is not an insect?

a. beetles
b. weevils
c. mouse
d. moths

7 The hole size a rat can fit through?

a. Half-dollar size
b. Quarter size
c. Penny sized
d. Quarter sized

8 When an employee has a service animal, they must do what after handling the animal?

a. Take it for a walk
b. Feed it
c. Wash their hands
d. Go home for the day

Chapter 13

Management Systems and Crisis Planning

Introduction

Running a safe and successful operation does not happen by accident. It requires careful planning and staff training, all of which must be documented and recorded. The management systems employed must be based on sound scientific principles in order to be confident food will be protected against the primary risk factors associated with foodborne illness. With these management documents and records in hand, the food operation can confidently operate and easily pass inspections.

Management must also plan for a crisis, such as fire, flooding, loss of power, and more. Having a plan in place allows decisions to be made more quickly and with confidence. With a well-prepared crisis management plan, the food operation can keep staff and food safe if remaining open is possible. Being able to remain open during a crisis can be a significant benefit to the local community who may not be able to prepare food in their homes or have been required to evacuate.

Key Terms

Keep an eye out for these essential topics:

- Risk
- Person in Charge (PIC)
- Active Managerial Control
- HACCP

- Prerequisite programs
- Hazard
- Critical control point (CCP)
- Imminent health hazard

Objectives

After working through this chapter, you should be able to explain the following to friends and family:

- Appreciate the responsibilities of the person in charge
- Describe the seven principles of a HACCP plan
- Explain what active managerial control is
- Understand the necessity of a crisis management plan
- Describe the events that necessitate the closure of the operation
- Explain the steps necessary to re-open after a crisis-based closure

Terry,
Food Safety Instructor

Terry smiled to himself. That was a great day, he thought to himself. Six years ago, he was working as a high school teacher and feeling burned out. His school had so many challenges that he didn't think he could continue working there. Did he regret that he left at the end of that school year? Absolutely. Terry really missed his students, as much as they drove him crazy at times, and they all had their issues; they were all great people, and he missed his connections. Once he left teaching, he didn't really know what else to do. He didn't have much in the way of savings, so he had to get something to pay the rent. The restaurant industry was where he landed. For the next couple of years, he bumped around from server jobs to being a terrible bartender, among other things. Eventually, he started as a server at a small French brasserie and was promoted to supervisor. He was given the opportunity to get his Food Safety Certification and decided that it may be worth his while. The boss offered him an extra three dollars an hour and guaranteed hours if he passed.

In the class, Terry excelled. He had purchased the textbook in advance and did a little pre-reading before the course to be prepared and immensely enjoyed it. He always had a very organized and almost scientific mind, so he found the material very interesting. When it came to the exam, he blew it out of the water. The instructor was so impressed she mentioned to him that he might want to consider looking at this being his new career. Half-jokingly, he blew it off at first. But that thought stayed with him. Maybe that is exactly what he is destined for. Six months later, Terry was shadowing another teacher in a classroom of nervous students. This time around, they were all adults, all paying good money to be there. A few weeks later, Terry was in the classroom by himself, teaching again and opening up opportunities for people every day. He loved his new career. Back in teaching, right where he belonged.

Programs to Manage Food Safety

A safe and successful food operation will maintain a series of programs or written procedures designed to ensure that laws are followed, and that food is safe to consume. Separating the totality of requirements into smaller manageable programs can help focus training, re-training, and future material reference, which improves staff retention and supports a consistent application. Breaking things down makes the requirements feel less overwhelming, and some staff may not need to be trained on every program when they first start on the job, if ever.

Examples of food safety management programs:

- Personal hygiene program
- Receiving and storage program
- Food safety program
- Time as a public health control program
- Cleaning and sanitization program
- Clean-up of vomiting and diarrheal events program
- Pest control program
- Facility maintenance program
- Crisis response program

These programs should be well documented, accessible to staff, and consistently reinforced through corrective action and examples. A manager might also acknowledge staff for doing a good job during performance reviews and in front of their peers to balance **corrective action** with positive reinforcement to achieve improved results.

Developed and implemented written procedures are essential in controlling **risk** factors associated with a food establishment. When all of these programs are in place, the **person in charge** (**PIC**) has **active managerial control** over the food establishment and complies with the Food Code.

References in this Coursebook:

Glossary reference: Orange text means the definition of the word can be found in the Glossary located in the Student Workbook.

Food Code section reference: To verify or further study topics covered in this Coursebook, the FDA Food Code section numbers are provided in the margins. The current version of the offical code may be download here:
https://www.fda.gov/food/retail-food-protection/fda-food-code

Person In Charge (PIC)

A primary responsibility of a **person in charge** (PIC) is compliance with the Food Code.

A business may give employees any number of titles and responsibilities. An employee is sometimes called partner, associate, assistant manager, manager, supervisor, executive chef, and more. When an inspector shows up, they will not care about a business title. They will want to speak with a person in charge.

> **KEY TERM**   **Person in charge (PIC)** means the individual present at a food establishment who is responsible for the operation at the time of inspection.

Becoming a PIC

Become a PIC by complying in one of three categories:

2-102.12
2-102.11

- Certification: The PIC is certified as a food protection manager
- Knowledge: The PIC correctly responds to questions about food safety practices and principles
- Compliance: When there are no violations noted during the inspection

A designated PIC must be on the premises any time the business operates. Failure to present one during an inspection is a serious infraction.

PIC Duties

2-103.11

The PIC performs these duties:

- Identifies hazards in the daily operation of the food establishment
- Develops and implements policies and procedures to prevent foodborne illness
- Trains employees about food safety and sanitation
- Directs food preparation activities and corrective actions to protect the health of the consumer
- Monitors daily operations to ensure that food safety policies and procedures are followed

PIC Responsibilities

The following summarization, which may read like an overview of this entire book, is an itemized list within the Food Code spelling out specific responsibilities of the PIC.

2-103.11

Private home prohibition

Food establishment operations are not conducted in a private home or a room used as living or sleeping quarters.

Limited access to food preparation areas

Persons unnecessary to the food establishment operation are not allowed in the food preparation, food storage, or dishwashing areas.

> **Exception**: the person in charge may authorize brief visits and tours if steps are taken to ensure that food and food-contact surfaces are not contaminated.

Persons with access comply with code

Employees and other persons such as delivery and maintenance persons and pesticide applicators entering the food preparation, food storage, and dishwashing areas comply with the Food Code.

Effective person hygiene

Employees are effectively cleaning their hands by routinely monitoring the employees' handwashing activities.

Following receiving procedures

Employees are visibly observing foods as they are received to determine that they are from approved sources, delivered at the required temperatures, protected from contamination, unadulterated, and accurately presented by routinely monitoring the employees' observations and periodically evaluating foods upon their receipt.

Overnight key-drop deliveries verified

Employees are verifying that foods delivered to the food establishment during non-operating hours are from approved sources and are placed into appropriate storage locations such that they are maintained at the required temperatures, protected from contamination, unadulterated, and accurately presented.

Cooking to minimum internal temperatures

Employees are properly cooking time/temperature control for safety food, being particularly careful in cooking those foods known to cause severe foodborne illness and death, such as eggs and comminuted meats, through daily oversight of the employees' routine monitoring of the cooking temperatures using appropriate and calibrated temperature measuring devices.

Rapid cooling effectively

Employees are using proper methods to rapidly cool time/temperature control for safety foods that are not held hot or are not for consumption within 4 hours, through daily oversight of the employees' routine monitoring of food temperatures during cooling.

Correct and consistent hold and cold holding temperatures

Employees are properly maintaining the temperatures of time/temperature control for safety foods during hot and cold holding through daily oversight of the employees' routine monitoring of food temperatures.

Ensuring safe thawing practices

Food employees are properly maintaining the temperature of TCS foods during thawing through daily oversight of their routine monitoring of food temperatures.

Consumer advisories

Consumers who order raw or partially cooked ready-to-eat foods of animal origin are informed that the food is not cooked sufficiently to ensure its safety.

Proper cleaning and sanitizing

Employees are correctly sanitizing cleaned multiuse equipment and utensils before they are reused through routine monitoring of solution temperature and exposure time for hot water sanitizing, and chemical concentration, pH, temperature, and exposure time for chemical sanitizing.

Self-service reuse awareness

Consumers are notified that clean tableware is to be used when they return to self-service areas such as salad bars and buffets.

No bare hand content with RTE foods

Except when approval is obtained from the regulatory authority, employees are preventing cross-contamination of ready-to-eat food with bare hands by properly using suitable utensils such as deli tissue, spatulas, tongs, single-use gloves, or dispensing equipment.

Basic food safety and allergy awareness training

Employees are adequately trained in food safety, including food allergy awareness, as it relates to their assigned duties. Food allergy awareness includes describing foods identified as major food allergens and the symptoms that they could cause in a sensitive individual who has an allergic reaction

Personal health notification responsibility

Food employees and conditional employees are informed in a verifiable manner of their responsibility to report per law, to the person in charge, information about their health and activities as they relate to diseases that are transmissible through food.

Required written procedures in place and on file

Written procedures and plans, where specified by the Food Code and as developed by the food establishment, are maintained and implemented as required.

Active Managerial Control

A manager or person in charge must always maintain **active managerial control** over the food establishment. This means they understand the law, know the staff has been properly trained, are aware of the various activities happening in the food establishment, and are prepared for an inspection at all times.

Based on research, the CDC has identified five major risk factors based on food preparation practices and employee behaviors. The FDA addresses controls for these risk factors and has additionally established five **public health interventions** to protect consumer health.

Five major foodborne illness risk factors:

- Food from unsafe sources
- Poor personal hygiene
- Inadequate cooking
- Improper holding temperatures
- Contaminated equipment

Public health interventions:

- Demonstration of knowledge
- Employee health controls
- Controlling hands as a vehicle of contamination
- Time and temperature parameters for controlling pathogens
- Consumer advisory

Active managerial control **minimizes these** risk factors associated with foodborne illness.

> **KEY TERM** **Risk** means the likelihood that an adverse health effect will occur within a population as a result of a hazard in a food.

When an inspection occurs, problems that have already occurred are identified and marked as violations. The manager must react to these problems, which may have already contaminated food or caused foodborne illness. By contrast, when a food manager has active managerial control, they proactively comply with the Food Code and mitigate the major food safety risks.

Hazard Analysis Critical Control Point (HACCP) Program

Annex 4, Page 4

Hazard Analysis and Critical Control Point (HACCP) is a voluntary systematic approach to identifying, evaluating, and controlling food safety risks. These hazards include food that has been contaminated by bad bugs (bacteria and viruses), chemicals, or physical objects (chapters 3 and 4) and is likely to cause foodborne illness when consumed. When the HACCP approach is embraced -- along with employee training, basic sanitation, and other prerequisite programs -- this **preventative** method assures active managerial control. The result is reduced risks and fewer violations during inspections.

Hazard **A**nalysis **C**ritical **C**ontrol **P**oint

- What are the food safety hazards
- Where do the hazards occur
- How are the hazards controlled
- Verify the process

KEY TERM HACCP plan means a written document that delineates the formal procedures for following the Hazard Analysis and Critical Control Point principles developed by The National Advisory Committee on Microbiological Criteria for Foods.

Prerequisite Programs

Annex 4, Page 5

An effective HACCP system must have a solid procedural foundation that covers a food establishment's basic operational and sanitation requirements. Collectively, these procedures are called **prerequisite programs**.

Prerequisite programs may include:

- Buyer specifications
- Vendor certification programs
- Training programs
- Allergen management
- Recipe/process instructions
- First-In-First-Out (FIFO) procedures
- Other Standard Operating Procedures (SOPs)

These prerequisite programs aim to:

- Prevent food contamination by biological, chemical, and physical hazards
- Control bacterial growth that can result from temperature abuse
- Maintain equipment

With effective prerequisite programs in place, controlling hazards associated with food and its preparation (i.e., a HACCP system) can receive more attention.

HACCP Principles

Based on a solid foundation of prerequisite programs, the following seven fundamental principles are used to accomplish the HACCP objective:

1. Determine the critical control points (CCPs)
2. Conduct a hazard analysis
3. Establish critical limits
4. Establish monitoring procedures
5. Establish corrective actions
6. Establish verification procedures
7. Establish record-keeping and documentation procedures

8-201.14(E)
Annex 4, Page 5

Figure 1

#1 - Determine the critical control points (CCPs)

Annex 4, Page 19

A **critical control point (CCP)** is a specific point in the flow of food where the loss of control may result in an unacceptable health risk. When essential to food safety, control measures identified in the previous principle (conduct a hazard analysis), such as minimum internal cook temperature for TCS foods, are usually applied at critical control points (CCPs) in the HACCP plan.

> **KEY TERM**
>
> **Critical control point** means a point or procedure in a specific food system where loss of control may result in an unacceptable health risk.

To ensure the prevention, elimination, or reduction (to safe levels) of identified hazards, each CCP will have control measures. Common examples of CCPs include cooking, cooling, hot holding, and cold holding of RTE/TCS foods. CCPs are not used for non-food safety concerns such as refrigerating non-TCS foods for freshness and quality-of-food control.

➔ The result identifies specific points in the process where hazards may occur.

#2 - Conduct a hazard analysis

Annex 4, Page 6

The purpose of hazard analysis is to develop a list of food safety hazards that are reasonably likely to cause illness or injury if not effectively controlled.

> **KEY TERM**
>
> **Hazard** means a biological, chemical, or physical property that may cause an unacceptable consumer health risk.

The process of conducting a hazard analysis involves two stages:

- Hazard Identification
- Hazard Evaluation

Hazard identification

8-101.14(D)

This hazard analysis stage involves reviewing the entire process, e.g., for a specific menu item, and identifying any potential hazards. The individuals involved observe the whole food-preparation process for a particular dish and brainstorm ways that ingredients, movements, equipment, or timing might permit hazards to contaminate food.

➔ The result is a list of potential hazards possible at each step in the food preparation process.

Hazard evaluation

This hazard evaluation stage ranks each listed item's severity and the likelihood of occurrence. For example, cross-contamination with a knife is more severe and likely than a piece of ceiling tile falling into food. Based on this information, a decision can be made on whether to control it in the HACCP plan. Hazards that are not reasonably likely to occur might not be considered in an HACCP plan.

➔ The result is a list of significant hazards and actions to control them. These actions -- called **control measures** -- are used to prevent, eliminate, or reduce a hazard.

#3 - Establish critical limits

A **critical limit** is a scientifically-based and measurable factor used to determine if food is safe or not. Each CCP has one or more critical limits, such as temperature, time, moisture level, water activity (a_w), or pH.

Annex 4, Page 22

> **KEY TERM**
> **Critical limit** means the maximum or minimum value to which a physical, biological, or chemical parameter must be controlled at a critical control point to minimize the risk that the identified food safety hazard may occur.

Critical limit **examples:**

● The critical limits for chicken are temperature and time, 165F (74C) for less than 1 second. These are *minimum* critical limits to eliminating or reducing pathogens to safe consumption levels.

● The critical limit for sushi rice is a pH of less than or equal to 4.6. This is a maximum critical limit to control the growth of spore-forming bacteria.

Critical limits must be scientifically-based and measurable. They can come from the FDA Food Code, other applicable guidelines, performance standards, or experimental results.

➔ The result is a defined, measurable value -- checked at a critical control point (CCP) -- used to determine if food is safe or not.

#4 - Establish monitoring procedures

Annex 4, Page 22

Once the critical limits are defined for each CCP, monitoring procedures are established to observe or measure food.

An example of monitoring is to **measure** the temperature immediately after the cook step, if cooking chicken is determined to be a CCP. Another example would be **observing** for physical contaminants when preparing food off-site, if this type of contaminant is identified as a CCP given the temporary structure and location.

Experienced staff should conduct monitoring activities, which are ideally performed continuously. If monitoring is intermittent, it should be done with a frequency necessary to ensure critical limits are met.

➔ The result is the definition of observing and taking measurements to determine if critical limits are being established and maintained.

#5 - Establish corrective actions

Annex 4, Page 23

Corrective action must be taken when a critical limit is not met. This is an activity performed by a food handler to ensure food is safe to consume. The response may involve additional cooking or the removal of a physical contaminant, such as a nutshell. If the food cannot be made safe, it must be discarded.

➔ The result is the documented actions required when critical limits are not met.

#6 - Establish verification procedures

Annex 4, Page 23

To show that an HACCP plan works, a **Verification** process is used. This validation activity focuses on collecting and evaluating scientific and technical information to determine if an HACCP plan will effectively control the hazard. These activities are performed frequently and include:

- Observe the person doing monitoring and keeping records and determine if done according to plan
- Ensure corrective action was taken when monitoring found and recorded a critical limit was not met
- Validating the established critical limits are achieving food safety results desired
- Confirming equipment is used, maintained, and calibrated properly

Clear instructions should be developed detailing who is responsible for conducting verification, the frequency of verification, and the procedures used.

➔ The result is clear instructions on how to verify the HACCP plan is working

#7 - Establish record-keeping and documentation procedures

Keeping records is an essential step in ensuring the continued safety of food. Records can be used to verify the HACCP plan is working. Patterns might also be identified that reveal where additional staff training might be needed. In the event of a confirmed disease outbreak, these records can help authorities narrow down the problem and more quickly contain the crisis.

Figure 2

Types of records maintained in support of food safety:

- Records documenting the activities related to the prerequisite programs
- Monitoring records
- Corrective action records
- Verification and validation records
- Calibration records

These records should be maintained on file in the food establishment for future reference. They should also be made available to an inspector upon request.

→ The result is a collection of records documenting the HACCP plan activities

Annex 4, Page 24

HACPP Essentials

An HACCP-based plan should be well organized and contain all the information and steps required to be a consistent application and training resource.

An HACCP plan should include the following elements:

- Name, address, and contact information for the food establishment
- The food item or type of food to be controlled with the HACCP plan
- For each food item, define the process flow, including:
  - List each step in the process
  - Identify the hazards and controls for each step
  - Document where the critical control points occur
  - List the ingredients and equipment required
  - CCP summary for each food item that identifies:
    - The critical limit for each CCP (e.g., time, temperature, or pH measurement)
    - Frequency and method of monitoring and controlling each CCP
    - Identify who is responsible for monitoring CCPs
    - When critical limits are not met, indicate corrective action required
    - To validate the HACCP plan is working, define records to be maintained
- List the necessary PIC steps if critical limits are not met for each CCP
- Include additional experiments or scientific data supporting food is not compromised and is safe for consumption

Crisis Preparedness

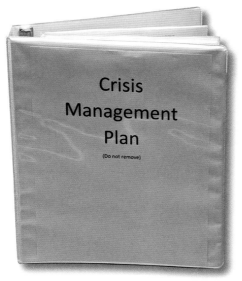

Figure 3

Many things can go wrong in the food service industry, which has been a theme throughout this book. The issues often have to do with food preparation practices and employee actions, which lead to foodborne illness. This can create a foodborne illness outbreak.

Additionally, things outside anyone's control can create an **imminent health hazard**, such as flooding, power outages, storms, and water/sewage system failures.

Each of these situations constitutes a crisis.

8-404

> **KEY TERM** **Imminent health hazard** means a significant threat or danger to health that is considered to exist when there is evidence sufficient to show that a product, practice, circumstance, or event creates a situation that requires immediate correction or cessation of operation to prevent injury based on:
>
> - The number of potential injuries
> - The nature, severity, and duration of the anticipated injury

A crisis must be tackled head-on regardless of who is at fault or what the financial or public relations ramifications might be. People's health and well-being are paramount. Having a plan and working with the authorities (e.g., health officials, CDC, hospitals, etc.) is always the best approach to effective crisis management.

Crisis Management Plan

A crisis management binder or intranet page should include:

1. Crisis management team
2. Crisis-communication plan
3. Foodborne incident response
4. Imminent health hazards response

Crisis management team

A group of individuals who — collectively -- have complete knowledge of the operation should be identified to serve on a crisis management team in an emergency. The size of this team will depend on the size and complexity of the food establishment. At the very least, it should include an individual who can make decisions on behalf of the business, someone who knows the flow of food, and someone with working knowledge of the facility. This might be a single person in a small operation.

Crisis-communication plan

When a crisis unfolds, a crisis-contact list is used to contact the crisis-management team. Everyone on this team should be kept up to date throughout the crisis.

This section of the plan should also have contact information for local media if an announcement needs to be made about an imminent health hazard.

The document should identify a spokesperson that is the only person who will speak to anyone outside the organization. This ensures there is a consistent and accountable message being delivered externally.

Foodborne incident response

When a foodborne illness is reported, it should be taken seriously. Staff should be trained to take a person's contact information, what they ate, and when. They should be sympathetic but not admit any wrongdoing. If a confirmed disease outbreak occurs, which means more than one person is affected, the authorities will investigate and determine the source of the problem.

If any food reported to have caused a foodborne illness is still in service, it should be labeled and removed. If an employee is suspected of being ill, they should be excluded.

A foodborne illness incident report should be available and filled out to aid in collecting pertinent information. Additionally, a manager should collect all logs immediately. This will ensure a food handler does not try to cover up any wrongdoing and will be ready to share with authorities.

Imminent health hazards response

8-404.11

Most people at home or working in a business don't know what to do when the power goes out, the water stops working, or sewage begins backing up. When these things happen in a food operation, the crisis management plan should have the answers. It should have the contact information for the local utilities and may have a series of If, Then situations to aid in how to respond to the event.

Ceasing Operations and Reporting

A food operation must immediately discontinue operations and notify the regulatory authority if an imminent health hazard may exist because of an emergency such as a: *Annex 3, 8-404.11*

- Fire
- Flood
- Extended interruption of:
  - ○ Electrical service
  - ○ Water service
  - ○ Sewage backup
- Misuse of poisonous or toxic materials
- The onset of an apparent foodborne illness outbreak
- Gross insanitary occurrence or condition
- Other circumstances that may endanger public health

Each of these should be treated as a crisis, following the crisis management plan.

A food establishment does not need to stop operations if they are unaffected by the imminent health hazard. For example, a fire in an adjacent building or a flood across town.

There are situations where an establishment can continue to operate during a crisis if its crisis plan was previously approved, corrective actions taken related to affected food, and the local authorities notified.

Resumption of Operations

If operations are discontinued, the permit holder shall obtain approval from the regulatory authority before resuming operations. *8-404.12*

Power Outage

8-404.11

Annex 3, Page 213

A real challenge for a food operation is when the power goes out or refrigeration fails. It affects critical infrastructure such as refrigeration, lights, and dishwashing machines. Sometimes, the establishment must close as it has no way of working. However, in a well-lit space in the middle of the day, it may be possible to remain open with a few precautions. Doing so may significantly benefit the community if they have also lost power and are less able to prepare food.

TCS foods are the primary concern during a power outage since time/temperature abuse can render the food unsafe for consumption.

Example of steps to document in a crisis management binder:

- Suspend all operations if there is an imminent personal safety or public health danger
- Notify the regulatory authority
- Call the power company to report the outage
- Keep a record of when the outage started and its duration
- Regularly check and record temperatures of TCS foods
- Calculate the time food has spent in the temperature danger zone
- Discard food that has spent more than 2 hours in the temperature danger zone
- Prepare an emergency menu to optimize resources

Refrigerator and freezer doors must be kept closed when not checking TCS food temperatures. Ice cubes, ice packs, or dry ice can keep TCS foods below 41°F (5°C). Do not add hot food to refrigerators or freezers during an outage, as this will increase the ambient temperature.

A power generator can provide power to critical areas if available. Using a generator presents dangers that should be considered, such as the location of extension cords and how it will be properly connected to the building's electrical system, so it does not pose a danger to local utility workers.

Hot food can be maintained hot with non-power heat sources, such as canned heat used for catering events.

Use non-power sources of heat, such as chafing dishes with canned heat, to maintain hot TCS food at 135°F (57°C).

Returning to regular operation may require the approval of the local regulatory authority. When power is restored, record the time, check the power panel circuit breakers, and monitor the refrigeration units to ensure they are functioning correctly.

Water Service Interruption

Loss of water can cause a significant disruption of service for a restaurant. Even a brief outage can create serious contamination issues due to a sudden loss of pressure and the possibility of backflow. Any disruption of water should result in careful monitoring of the water supply and a call to the water supply utility. However, even with a total water loss, it may be possible to remain operational when a crisis management plan is in place. Again, this may significantly benefit the community if they have also lost water and cannot prepare food.

8-404.11

Annex 3, Page 213

Food safety is the primary concern during a water outage.

Example of steps to document in a crisis management binder:

- Suspend all operations if there is an imminent personal safety or public health danger
- Notify the regulatory authority
- Call the water company to report the disruption of service
- Keep a record of when the outage started and its duration
- Maintain an inventory of bottled water
- Maintain contact list for service providers: water, ice, plumber, etc.
- Develop a contingency plan for toilets and handwashing
- Prepare an emergency menu to optimize resources

All food preparation must cease if an alternative handwashing station is not available. Otherwise, only pre-packaged food may be served. When serving only pre-packaged food, hand antiseptics or chemically treated towelettes must be used to clean hands.

Returning to regular operation may require the approval of the local regulatory authority. When water is restored, record the time and open the taps until the water runs clear. If closed due to an imminent health hazard, the operation may not re-open until authorization has been granted.

Sewage Backup

A sewage backup is a significant health risk since it contains dangerous pathogens and can contaminate food. The operation must be immediately suspended when there is a persistent sewage backup in the kitchen. A sewage backup due to neglected equipment or facility maintenance is not considered a crisis.

8-404.11

Annex 3, Page 213

> **KEY TERM**
>
> Sewage means liquid waste containing animal or vegetable matter in suspension or solution and may include liquids containing chemicals in solution.

Food safety is the primary concern during a sewage backup.

Example of steps to document in a crisis management binder:

- Suspend all operations if there is an imminent personal safety or public health danger
- Notify the regulatory authority
- Call the local utility to report the problem
- Maintain a contact list of service providers, such as a plumber, drain specialist, facility cleaner
- Identify emergency shut-off valves and back siphonage preventers
- Maintain an inventory of cleaning supplies
- Require double handwashing after cleaning and before working with food
- Develop a contingency plan for toilets, if affected
- Define alternate options for warewashing and affected sinks
- Discard all contaminated food

Affected areas, including toilets, should be closed off and posted to prevent access.

Returning to regular operation may require the approval of the local regulatory authority. If closed due to an imminent health hazard, the operation may not re-open until authorization has been granted. All affected areas, equipment, and food-contact surfaces must be cleaned and sanitized. Contaminated food must be discarded.

Flooding

8-404.11

Annex 3, Page 213

Following a flood, the crisis management plan should be used to navigate the challenge. Flood waters can contain pathogens that may be the source of contamination and result in foodborne illness. Significant cleaning and sanitizing must occur and may require the help of a professional service.

Food safety is the primary concern after a flood event.

Example of steps to document in a crisis management binder:

- Suspend all operations if there is an imminent personal safety or public health danger
- Notify the regulatory authority
- Maintain a contact list of service providers, such as a plumber, drain specialist, facility cleaner
- Identify emergency shut-off valves and back siphonage preventers
- Maintain an inventory of cleaning supplies
- Develop a contingency plan for toilets, if affected
- Discard all contaminated food
- Clean and sanitize all affected equipment and food-contact surfaces

During a flood event, e.g., a water main break, if the flooding can be isolated to a specific area, the operation may be able to remain open. The parameters needed to make this decision should be itemized on the crisis management plan.

Returning to regular operation may require the approval of the local regulatory authority. If closed due to an imminent health hazard, the operation may not re-open until authorization has been granted. All affected areas, equipment, and food-contact surfaces must be cleaned and sanitized. Contaminated food must be discarded.

Fire Event

Major fires that contaminate food or food-production areas must be handled according to a preplanned crisis management system. This does not include small non-reported fires extinguished with wet towels or a handheld extinguisher where food is not contaminated.

8-404.11

Annex 3, Page 213

Food safety is the primary concern after a fire event.

Figure 4

Example of steps to document in a crisis management binder:

- Suspend all operations if there is an imminent personal safety or public health danger
- Notify the regulatory authority
- Work with the regulatory authority to determine what must be discarded
- Clean and sanitize the affected areas

Heat, smoke, and fire extinguishing chemicals can affect packaging and containers.

What to throw away:

- Exposed food or food stored in cardboard, plastic wrap, foil, paper, and in containers with lids
- Food in refrigerators and freezers if contaminated, since door seals are not airtight
- Stored ice in ice bins or ice makers
- TCS foods if in the temperature danger zone for more than four hours
- Single-service and single-use items
- Food or products observed to be contaminated or damaged

Returning to regular operation may require the approval of the local regulatory authority. All affected areas, equipment, and food-contact surfaces must be cleaned and sanitized. Contaminated food must be discarded.

Summary

The manager or person in charge is responsible for maintaining active managerial control of the food operation at all times. In addition to basic prerequisite programs such as personal hygiene and cleaning schedules, an HACCP plan can be used to identify, monitor, and verify major risk factors related to food safety. Doing so eliminates or maintains hazards at safe levels, where food is safe to consume.

Seven fundamental principles of an HACCP plan:

1. Conduct a hazard analysis
2. Determine the critical control points (CCPs)
3. Establish critical limits
4. Establish monitoring procedures
5. Establish corrective actions
6. Establish verification procedures
7. Establish record-keeping and documentation procedures

No one can predict when a disaster or emergent event will occur. Therefore, the management team should have a crisis management plan in place in order to respond quickly and keep food safe. Doing so will prevent foodborne illness, be a service to the community, and limit the loss of revenues due to food contamination.

Reasons to suspend operations:

- Fire
- Flood
- Extended interruption of:
- Electrical service
- Water service
- Sewage backup
- Misuse of poisonous or toxic materials
- The onset of an apparent foodborne illness outbreak
- Gross insanitary occurrence or condition
- Other circumstances that may endanger public health

The Student's Workbook

As assigned by your instructor, use the separate Student's Workbook to work independently or in groups.

Activities for this week's chapter include:

- Design an HACCP plan for chicken alfredo
- Watch the video and reflect
- Discuss the risks of each ingredient in the alfredo dish recipe
- Make a list of equipment needed
- Produce the recipe
- Review the cleaning and sanitizing checklist

Review Questions

Use these questions to check your knowledge of the material in this chapter. Your instructor has the answers.

1 Which is not a requirement of a person in charge (PIC)?

a. Knowledgeable
b. Job title: manager
c. Certified
d. Compliant

2 When staff are trained, and systems are in place, the PIC has

a. Critical control points defined
b. A crisis management plan
c. An HACCP plan
d. Active managerial control

3 Which is not a major foodborne illness risk:

a. Out of order toilets
b. Food from unsafe sources
c. Improper holding temperatures
d. Contaminated equipment

4 Which plan is used in the event of an emergency:

a. Federal FEMA plan
b. Cleaning plan
c. Food defense plan
d. Crisis management plan

5 The first HACCP principle is:

a. Hazard analysis
b. Be covered to keep water out
c. Be painted green
d. Have at least three walls and a gate

6 A crisis management plan should include a

a. Crisis management team
b. Foodborne illness incident reported
c. Crisis communication plan
d. All of the above

7 An operation does not need to shut down for

a. A small isolated fire
b. Sewage backup in the kitchen
c. Contaminated water supply
d. Extensive flooding

8 An operation must shut down if the following happens:

a. Sewage backed up in a single sink
b. A small isolated fire
c. Sewage backup in the kitchen
d. Power goes out for 5 min.

Chapter 14

Regulations, Inspections, & Staff Training

Introduction

A food safety manager has a lot of responsibilities, but some of the most important are covered in this chapter. It is not to say that staff training is more important than cooking chicken properly or preventing cross-contamination. However, if food handlers are not trained on the applicable rules (regulations) and what the rule enforcer (inspector) will look for, everything else will surely fail.

This chapter looks at the various governmental agencies involved in creating the Food Code and related regulations and how they are adopted and enforced in the United States. An interesting thing to be aware of is that the FDA Food Code is not a federal law, which means each jurisdiction (usually a state or tribal nation) has the authority to enact its own Food Code. Many choose to use the FDA Food Code or a slightly modified version. However, some have a unique version, making it critical to train even experienced staff as their experience may not be one hundred percent relevant.

Key Terms

Keep an eye out for these essential topics:

- Food and Drug Administration (FDA)
- FDA Food Code
- USDA Food Safety and Inspection Service (FSIS)
- Centers for Disease Control (CDC)
- Certified food protection manager
- Regulatory inspections
- Priority item
- Skills assessment

Objectives

After working through this chapter, you should be able to explain the following to friends and family:

- Describe the governmental entities involved in food
- Learn about the inspection process
- Explore how inspection violations must be handled
- Explain the general timeline of an inspection report
- Understand the benefits of staff training
- Describe the training methods

Jayda,
Assistant Manager

Jayda had worked in the hospitality industry for a few years now. She got her start while she was studying Culinary Arts in high school and worked her way up through the ranks in the kitchen of several chain restaurants once she completed her associate's degree in Food Service. She enjoyed the creativity and camaraderie of working in the environment. Only six weeks ago she started her new job as an assistant manager at an Italian chain restaurant. She knew that they have restaurants all over the US, so if she wanted to travel while she was young, it could give her the opportunity to transfer to other locations in the future and move with a job.

Her first full week was fun, as she learned the ropes in the front-of-house, with the dining room and bar business being consistently busy most days for lunch and dinner. It seemed to be fun, until day five. That's when she noticed that the food distributor truck had dropped the food supplies off at the back door during lunch service. As always it was busy, but at 2 pm she noticed that all the food was still laying out. Not wanting to make trouble, she stepped over to the head chef and quietly commented on her concern as that food had now been out of refrigeration for over two hours. The chef was not in a good mood and barked at her that it was not at the top of his priorities and that maybe she should put it away if she were so concerned.

Taken aback, she did exactly that. It was after that, that she started to notice other issues when she would go back to collect food from the kitchen to serve. The kitchen was fairly large and well equipped. All set up to corporate specifications and relatively new. However, it was more about the habits that were the issues. The hand washing sinks always seemed to be a dumping ground. Sometimes dirty plates and silverware during service. Other times the deliveries would block them too. This bothered Jayda. She knew that this meant staff doesn't wash their hands as regularly as they should.

A couple of nights later the restaurant was packed and the kitchen was down one, as one of the sandwich station chefs was out sick. Jayda was trying to assist the others, adding sides like fruit and slaw to some of the plates, when she was running food out to the service team. That's when she noticed the shambles in the refrigerators. As we all know, refrigerators must be organized with ready-to-eat foods at the top and a regimented order for everything else. Everything must also be correctly wrapped and dated. This was definitely not happening. After service, she approached the head chef again. This time he ordered her out of "his kitchen". She was now questioning whether she made a good decision working in the restaurant at all.

All this was answered two days later when the health inspector arrived at the front desk. Lunch service was busy and everyone was bustling around. Jayda was off and enjoying her morning shopping with a friend. When she arrived later for her evening shift she heard all about the catastrophe that ensued. The health inspector had quietly settled into the kitchen and observed for the first few minutes, watching staff not washing their hands and handling RTE foods with bare hands. That set him off and he demanded the chef stop the kitchen. The chef refused and started arguing with the inspector about how much power he really had. As the inspector started to delve into the refrigerators he saw one infraction after another. Once he came back to the dishwashing station, he saw multiple cross-contamination issues between clean and dirty items, and finally when he realized that the kitchen was completely out of sanitizer, he was done. He ordered that lunch service be halted. Everything that Jayda had been concerned about was on the inspection report. By the time Jayda arrived for her shift, the restaurant was looking for a new head chef as well. All of these infractions being allowed under his watch were gross misconduct. He was neglecting the safety of every customer and the staff who ate there every day. Jayda was happy to be on the new safety committee created during the following weeks and worked to improve conditions. She is now proud to work in a great restaurant with a very high sanitation rating.

Regulations

The regulations and authority related to food establishments are helpful for a manager to understand. This allows them to be sure they comply with the law and follow the best guidance based on current science and understanding of food safety.

Government agencies involved in food safety:

- U.S. Department of Health and Human Services (HHS)
  - U.S. Public Health Services (PHS)
    - Food and Drug Administration (FDA)
    - Centers for Disease Control (CDC)
- U.S. Department of Agriculture (USDA)
- Local, state, tribal, and federal regulators

These governmental bodies are all funded by tax or tribal dollars with the directive to maintain the safety of food in the United States and Tribal Nations. However, the responsibility of protecting food from contamination must be shared between industry, regulating authorities, and consumers. Everyone must play a part in this critical public health initiative.

Figure 1

Food and Drug Administration (FDA)

The **Food and Drug Administration (FDA)** is a federal agency within the U.S. Department of Health and Human Services, with a mission to ensure the safety of all food except meat, poultry, and some egg products. As the department name implies, they oversee other things such as tobacco, drugs, medical devices, and more. With over 18 thousand employees, the FDA's efforts related to foods account for 18% of an annual budget of over $6 billion.

The FDA operates under the authority of several enacted laws passed by the U.S. Congress. Within the scope of these laws, the FDA creates regulations that become law after being posted for public comment.

8-101.10

The FDA developed the model **FDA Food Code**. The intent of the Food Code is to safeguard public health and provide consumers with safe, unadulterated, and honestly presented food, whether purchased or donated. Additionally, the FDA **periodically inspects** registered facilities that process food meant for interstate commerce.

Preface, Page ii

The FDA Food Code is **not a federal law** or regulation, as it does not have this authority within states or tribal municipalities. The Food Code is, however, the FDA's best advice for a uniform regulation system and is designed to simplify municipal adoption. Once a local, state, tribal, or federal body adopts the Food Code or an adaptation, it becomes law.

The current version of the Food Code can be found at this URL: https://www.fda.gov/food/retail-food-protection/fda-food-code

U.S. Department of Agriculture (USDA)

The U.S. Department of Agriculture's **Food Safety and Inspection Service (FSIS)** regulates aspects of the safety and labeling of traditional (non-game) meats, poultry, and certain egg products. The USDA also regulates and inspects the interstate distribution of food. FSIS is mandated to conduct **continuous inspections** of meat and poultry processing plants.

The USDA had nearly 100 thousand employees and a $150 billion budget in 2020.

Learn more about USDA's Food Safety and Inspection Service at this URL: https://www.fsis.usda.gov/

Centers for Disease Control (CDC)

The **Centers for Disease Control (CDC)** is a federal agency within the U.S. Department of Health and Human Services, with a mission to increase the health security of the U.S.

The CDC's role in food safety includes:

- Investigating multistate confirmed disease outbreaks
- Implementing systems to prevent illnesses better and detect and stop outbreaks
- Conducting research to determine the primary sources of foodborne illnesses and annual changes in the number of illnesses
- Helping state and local health departments improve the tracking and investigation of foodborne diseases and outbreaks

- Using data to determine whether prevention measures are working and where further efforts and additional targets for prevention are needed to reduce food-borne illness

- Working with other countries and international agencies to improve the tracking, investigation, and prevention of foodborne infections in the United States and around the world

The CDC, working with the FDA and USDA-FSIS, may take several actions during a multistate foodborne outbreak, including:

- Conduct traceback investigation to identify the source and distribution of contaminated food

- Inspect food processing facilities and farms and review their food safety protocols

- Collect samples from foods, food facilities, and farms for testing

- Request that companies recall contaminated food

Local, State, Tribal, and Federal Regulators

Each state has authority over food safety rules and regulations for food establishments.

- State/Tribal Nation
  - Writes or adopts Food Code
  - Writes or adopts building code
- City/County
  - Enforces state/tribal law
    - Inspections
    - Permits/Licenses: Building, Food, Alcohol
    - Certificate of occupancy
    - Granting variances
    - Approving HACCP plans
  - Optionally, adds new or creates more restrictive laws

In larger cities, the city government enforces building and food safety regulations. The state or county government oversees them in smaller towns and rural areas. The local regulating authority, often called the Health Department, has Health Inspectors who inspect food operations for compliance (covered later in this chapter).

Some states will adopt the FDA Food Code entirely, others will adopt a modified version, and some will write something entirely unique. This inconsistency in law within the United States creates challenges for the industry in its efforts to support food safety through training, technology, and equipment advancements, as well as for national chains operating in multiple states. A food manager must ensure they understand the rules and regulations in their region and each location; one may be within the city limits and another just outside.

Inspections

Food establishment inspections are an essential activity a manager and staff should appreciate and support to help ensure food is safe, and business can continue to run smoothly. **Regulatory inspections** and follow-up activities focus on effective managerial control and the effectiveness of the primary public health interventions addressed throughout the Food Code.

Public health interventions:

- Demonstration of knowledge
- Employee health controls
- Controlling hands as a vehicle of contamination
- Time and temperature parameters for controlling pathogens
- Consumer advisory

Figure 2

Inspections are always unannounced (i.e., surprise inspection) and at various times to allow different activities within the operation to be observed. They will likely have reviewed previous inspection reports and the menu better to understand the food operation and any critical hazards to look for. One of the first things they will likely do is a quick walkthrough of the entire facility to see which activities are currently happening that may not be happening later, such as receiving, food preparation, cooking, cooling, or reheating.

Throughout the inspection, they will watch for proper handwashing, condition and use of sinks, food preparation activities, cross-contact or contamination issues, cleaning and sanitization practices, and more.

Compliance with the "demonstration of knowledge" intervention involves accurately answering questions throughout the inspection and establishing one's ability to be identified as a PIC. One PIC demonstration method is being a **certified food protection manager**.

Frequency of Inspections

If a municipality (regulatory authority) has adopted the FDA Food Code, the frequency of inspections performed by the health inspector is specified in the Food Code.

8-401.10

- The regulatory authority shall inspect a food establishment at least once every 6 months.

Temporary Food Establishments

Inspections are performed periodically throughout the permit period for a temporary food establishment. Visits are likely to be more frequent if using improvised facilities or inexperienced food employees.

Decreased Frequency

The Food Code provides reasons for decreasing the number of inspections as follows:

- The regulatory authority may increase the inspection frequency beyond 6 months if:
  - The food establishment is fully operating under an approved and validated HACCP plan
  - Written risk-based inspection and contacted by telephone once every 6 months
  - Establishments only serving coffee and snacks, such as chips, nuts, popcorn, and pretzels

Increased Frequency

The Food Code provides reasons for increasing the number of inspections as follows:

- Past performance
  - Nonconformance with the Food Code or HACCP plan
  - Multiple or repeat violations
  - Legitimized complaints
- Type of operation and particular hazards
- Number of people served
- Highly susceptible population (HSP) served

Inspection Authority

8-402

The inspector has the legal authority to conduct an inspection of a food establishment during hours of operation and other reasonable times.

When an inspector first arrives, identifies themself, and states their intent to conduct an inspection, the PIC should ask to see their **official credentials**. At this point, the regulatory authority must be allowed to determine if the establishment complies with the Food Code through an inspection and the requested information and records. Access should never be denied because it is during rush hour, or a large delivery just arrived, etc.

Requested records may include:

- Temperature logs
- Cleaning and sanitization logs
- Purchasing and Receiving/temperature logs
- HACCP records

Questions the inspector may ask:

- How do you set up a 3-compartment sink
- How do you prevent cross-contact
- Describe your receiving procedures
- Where are your toxic chemicals stored

The PIC should be cooperative and accompany the inspector. This allows the PIC to ask questions or point out something the inspector may have overlooked or misread. Understanding the reason for any violations will help ensure the issue is fixed the first time correctly.

Inspection Report

8-403

The inspector is required to document their inspection. The document must include the name, location, date, and other information such as utility details, the status of the permit, and required personal certifications.

Figure 3

The report will also include any factual observations of violations or deviations from the Food Code requiring corrective action, including:

- Failure of the PIC to demonstrate the knowledge of foodborne illness prevention, application of HACCP principles, and the requirements of the Food Code

- Failure of food employees, conditional employees, and the PIC to report a disease or medical condition

- Nonconformance with priority items or priority foundation items of the Food Code

- Failure of the appropriate food employees to demonstrate their knowledge of and ability to perform per the procedural, monitoring, verification, and corrective action practices required by the inspector

- Failure of the PIC to provide records required by the inspector for determining conformance with an HACCP plan

- Nonconformance with critical limits of an HACCP plan

The report must include the time frame for corrective action (more on this in a moment). A copy of the report must be provided to the PIC, and the PIC must sign a receipt acknowledging they received it. The final report is a public document that can be made available to anyone who requests it.

Time Frame for Correction

The Food Code specifies the time frame violations need to be corrected based on the severity relative to food safety. There are three levels of severity defined and referenced throughout the Food Code.

8-403.20

Three risk-based control categories in the Food Code:

- **Priority item** is a provision in the Food Code whose application contributes directly to the elimination, prevention, or reduction to an acceptable level, hazards associated with foodborne illness or injury, and there is no other provision that more directly controls the hazard

- **Priority foundation item** is a provision in the Food Code whose application supports, facilitates, or enables one or more Priority Items.

- **Core item** is a provision in the Food Code that is not designated as a Priority Item or a Priority Foundation Item and that usually relates to general sanitation, operational controls, sanitation standard operating procedures (SSOPs), facilities or structures, equipment design, or general maintenance.

Priority Items and Priority Foundation Items, as well as any critical limits not met for an HACCP plan, must be corrected at the time of the inspection, meaning immediately. Clearly, an inspector cannot let any undercooked chicken be served to customers.

Some corrective actions may take more time depending on the nature of the potential hazard involved. In these cases the Food Code gives the following time limits:

<table>
<tr><th>Violation severity</th><th>Time frame</th></tr>
<tr><td>Priority Item</td><td>72 hours</td></tr>
<tr><td>Priority Foundation Item</td><td>10 calendar days</td></tr>
<tr><td>HACCP plan deviation</td><td>10 calendar days</td></tr>
<tr><td>Core Item</td><td>90 calendar days</td></tr>
</table>

8-405.11(B)(1)
8-405.11(B)(2)
8-405.11(B)(2)
8-406-11(A)

When violations have been resolved, the inspector is notified and makes another visit to observe the corrections. Once verified, the inspector updates the report to indicate the violations have been corrected.

Ceasing Operations

8-404

According to the Food Code, a food establishment shall immediately discontinue operations and notify the regulatory authority if an imminent health hazard may exist because of an emergency, such as:

- Fire or Flood
- Extended interruption of electrical or water service
- Sewage backup
- Considerable pest infestation
- Misuse of poisonous or toxic materials
- Onset of an apparent foodborne illness outbreak
- Significant unsanitary occurrence or condition, or
- Other circumstances that may endanger public health

Should any of these conditions be discovered during an inspection, the health inspector has the authority (in some jurisdictions) to require the establishment to cease operations by suspending their permit or license.

Staff Training

One of the most important duties of a food manager is training staff. If staff does not understand the major food safety interventions, they can't possibly be expected to avoid them effectively. Consistent and proper training is the only way to have active managerial control and benefit from the preventive nature of an HACCP plan. When working with untrained or inexperienced staff, problems are bound to follow as the manager cannot be everywhere all at once.

2-103.11

Annex 2, Page 65

Managers must be consistent with all aspects of staff training to ensure they are not discriminating against anyone.

Figure 4

Assessment

When new employees start working for a food establishment, they should be given a **skills assessment**. This helps the manager focus the training on training needs and things unique to the establishment.

Ways to administer an assessment:

- Verbally: asking a series of questions
- Written: printed quiz
- Software: answer questions on a computer
- Service: let a third party do the assessment

Even with senior staff, it is best never to assume how much a new person knows about food safety, especially if their experience is not local, given the possible differences across the U.S. and globally.

Training Program

Given the importance of safety and the many written programs required to prevent foodborne illness, it is easy to understand that a quality training program must be developed, documented, and implemented.

Training delivery methods:

- Videos
- Reading
- Hands-on
- On-the-job
- Outsourced

Given the many different learning styles, it is often best to use each method in a way that has some overlap and reinforces important concepts. New hires with previous experience might

Figure 5

start with company-standards videos and then move directly to on-the-job training.

Software-based training often uses a Learning Management System (LMS), which keeps track of an individual's progress, including where they stopped, and can present quizzes to ascertain comprehension.

Most large national restaurant chains will have a robust training program to ensure consistency across all locations. Training material should remain accessible to staff in the future in case they want to refresh their memory or understanding of a topic.

2-103.11(0)

Managers must ensure that their training programs, at the very least, cover topics required of employees by the Food Code, such as food safety and allergy awareness.

Corrective Action

Although its primary purpose is to ensure food safety, corrective action is also an excellent just-in-time teaching opportunity. But this is only effective if applied consistently. Suppose one instance of cross-contamination is cleaning, discarding food, and retraining; another is only cleaning and reconditioning the food. In that case, the employee attitude around the issue will be weak, and food contamination will likely occur more often.

Food Allergy Awareness

Starting with the 2022 Food Code, there is a specific requirement that the person in charge ensure employees are trained on food allergy awareness as it relates to their assigned duties. Food allergy awareness includes describing foods identified as major food allergens and the symptoms that a major food allergen could cause in a sensitive individual who has an allergic reaction. Staff is not expected to pass a test.

2-103.11(O)

Training topics will vary based on menu and procedures but might include:

Annex 3, Page 18

- Risks of offering food containing major food allergens
- Identification of the major food allergens and the hazards they present
- Recognition of symptoms of an allergic reaction and how to respond
- Food allergen ingredient identification and labeling
- Principles of cross-contact prevention concerning the major food allergens

Retraining

To emphasize the importance of food safety in a food establishment, violations of any of the foundation items should be quickly met with corrective action and some portion of retraining.

Annual training can also be provided to ensure staff stays current on the requirements specific to that establishment. Special training topics might be developed in response to a local issue (e.g., food defense issue) or an inspection violation.

Training Records

Records should be kept on all training activities. They can be used to ensure everyone has the same level of training and possibly shared with the inspector if appropriate.

- Trainee name, employee number, and date
- Topic trained on
- Notes, if applicable (e.g., late, absent, disagreed)

Training by Example

Management, the PIC, and senior management must reinforce training by setting a good example. Staff will notice if some people do not wash their hands or wear protective coverings. Setting a good example, along with consistent corrective action and retraining, will clarify how important food safety is to everyone. Fostering this culture will pay off by avoiding revenue/product loss and unwanted attention from people getting sick from eating contaminated food.

Summary

The food safety manager must be able to demonstrate their knowledge during an inspection. To do this, they must be trained, understand the applicable rules, and be cooperative with an inspector. The inspector will also ask staff questions about what they are doing, so staff also need to be trained.

Staff training is a critical mechanism that ties everything necessary about food safety together. When adequately developed and implemented, a staff training program will be the solid foundation for a successful business for many years!

Time frame for Food Code violation corrections:

- Priority Item   72 hours
- Priority Foundation Item   10 calendar days
- HACCP plan deviation   10 calendar days
- Core Item   90 calendar days

The Student's Workbook

As assigned by your instructor, use the separate Student's Workbook to work independently or in groups.

Activities for this week's chapter include:

- Introduce Culinary Math challenges
- Understand the importance of calculating yield and purchase amounts
- Watch the video and reflect
- Discuss the risks of each ingredient in the fruit display recipe
- Make a list of equipment needed
- Produce the recipe
- Review the cleaning and sanitizing checklist
- Work out ingredient yields

Use these questions to check your knowledge of the material in this chapter. Your instructor has the answers.

1 The agency that created and maintained the Food Code?

a. U.S. Department of Agriculture (USDA)

b. Food and Drug Administration (FDA)

c. Centers for Disease Control (CDC)

d. Red Lake Nation

2 The agency that inspects multistate foodborne illness outbreaks?

a. U.S. Department of Agriculture (USDA)

b. Food and Drug Administration (FDA)

c. USDA Food Safety and Inspection Service (FSIS)

d. Centers for Disease Control (CDC)

3 Agency that inspects meats, poultry, and certain egg products?

a. U.S. Department of Agriculture (USDA)

b. Food and Drug Administration (FDA)

c. USDA Food Safety and Inspection Service (FSIS)

d. Centers for Disease Control (CDC)

4 Who adopts a food code to make it legally binding?

a. City Government

b. County Government

c. State/Tribal Nation Government

d. Federal Government

5 A food manager should first ask an inspector:

a. To see official credentials

b. How long the inspection takes

c. If they need to use the restroom

d. Which records would they like to see

6 Which is not a cause for increased frequency of inspections?

a. HSP served

b. Size of operation

c. Previous inspection violations

d. Upper floor level operation

7 When is an inspection report provided?

a. At the conclusion of the inspection

b. Within ten days

c. Within 90 days

d. No time limit

Index

References in this Coursebook:

Glossary reference: Orange text means the definition of the word can be found in the Glossary located in the Student Workbook.

Food Code section reference: To verify or further study topics covered in this Coursebook, the FDA Food Code section numbers are provided in the margins. The current version of the offical code may be download here: https://www.fda.gov/food/retail-food-protection/fda-food-code